Fundamentals of Engineering Metallurgy

Fundamentals of Engineering Metallurgy

F. W. J. BAILEY

B.Sc.(Hons.), A.I.M. Senior Lecturer in the
Department of Mechanical and Production
Engineering, The North Gloucestershire
Technical College, Cheltenham; formerly
Technical Assistant to Manager Hot Roll-
ing Dept., Henry Wiggin and Co., Ltd.,
Birmingham; formerly Research Metallur-
gist with the Mond Nickel Co., Ltd.,
Birmingham

CASSELL · LONDON

CASSELL & COMPANY LTD
EDUCATIONAL DEPARTMENT
35 Red Lion Square · London WC1

and at

MELBOURNE · SYDNEY · TORONTO · CAPE TOWN
AUCKLAND

––––

© Cassell & Co. Ltd., 1961

First published 1961

Printed in Great Britain by
The Camelot Press Ltd., London and Southampton

F. 261

CONTENTS

v

PREFACE

The object of this book is to provide a short account of the fundamentals of Engineering Metallurgy. The author wishes to emphasize that the book has been written for the engineering student and not for the metallurgist. The study of Engineering Metallurgy requires a different approach from that of other engineering subjects, and this, together with the peculiar terminology of the metallurgist, creates special difficulties, particularly to a student with a limited background of physics and chemistry. In view of this, certain chapters have been deliberately simplified and details of metallurgical theories omitted. Wherever possible, simple diagrams have replaced long discussions.

It is hoped that students for the Higher National Certificates in Mechanical and Production Engineering will derive benefit from this treatment. Certain portions of the book should also prove useful to those studying for the Final City and Guilds of London Institute's Certificate in Machine Shop Engineering.

It is not possible to cover all aspects of the subject in a short book, and the author has, therefore, omitted details of production processes and mechanical testing.

The author wishes particularly to thank his colleague Mr. R. Kershaw, B.Sc.(Eng.) Hons., A.M.I.Mech.E., for drawing the diagrams and making many helpful suggestions.

The author wishes to thank the City and Guilds of London Institute for permission to publish past questions from the Final City and Guilds Examination in Machine Shop Engineering, and the Joint Committee for National Certificates and Diplomas in Mechanical Engineering for permission to include past questions which have been set for the Higher National Certificates in Mechanical and Production Engineering at the North Gloucestershire Technical College, Cheltenham.

Thanks are also due to Messrs. Edward Arnold (Publishers) Ltd., for the loan of a block from *Introduction to Metallic Corrosion* by Dr. U. R. Evans, and to Messrs. Kelvin and Hughes (Industrial) Ltd., for permission to reproduce diagrams from their publication *Kelvin and Hughes Ultrasonic Flaw Detector Mark 5*. Details of etching reagents for the macro- and microscopical examination of metals and alloys given in Chapter 15 have been mainly taken from *Photomicrography with the Vickers Projection Microscope* by kind permission of the publishers Messrs. Cooke, Troughton and Simms Ltd.

The author of a general textbook depends for much of his information on the work of other more specialized publications. Many of the latter are mentioned in the comprehensive bibliography and the author wishes to acknowledge their assistance, and recommends them to students for further reading. If any omission has been made, or if due acknowledgement has not been given, the author tenders his sincere apologies to the individuals or authorities concerned.

F. W. J. BAILEY

ABBREVIATIONS USED IN THE TEXT

Ag	= Silver	Mo	= Molybdenum
Al	= Aluminium	Ni	= Nickel
As	= Arsenic	P	= Phosphorus
Be	= Beryllium	Pb	= Lead
B	= Boron	S	= Sulphur
C	= Carbon	Sb	= Antimony
Cd	= Cadmium	Se	= Selenium
Ce	= Cerium	Si	= Silicon
Co	= Cobalt	Sn	= Tin
Cr	= Chromium	Ti	= Titanium
Cu	= Copper	TC	= Total Carbon
Fe	= Iron	V	= Vanadium
Mg	= Magnesium	W	= Tungsten
Mn	= Manganese	Zn	= Zinc
		Zr	= Zirconium

U.T.S. = Ultimate Tensile Strength in tons per square inch
t.s.i. = Tons per Square Inch
EL = Percentage Elongation on $4\sqrt{A}$ gauge length
R.A. = Percentage Reduction of Area
Y.P. = Yield Point in tons per square inch
L.P. = Limit of Proportionality in tons per square inch
P.S. = Proof Stress (0·1% or 0·2% as stated) in tons per square inch
B.H.N. = Brinell Hardness Number
V.P.N. = Vickers Pyramid Numeral (Hardness)

IMPORTANT PHYSICAL PROPERTIES OF SOME PURE METALS

Metal	Symbol	Melting Point °C.	Density gram/ml	Specific Heat cal/gram/C°	Coefficient of Linear Expansion $\times 10^6$ at 20°C.	Thermal Conductivity C.G.S. Units	Electrical Resistivity microhm. cm.
Aluminium	Al	660	2·7	0·215	23·0	0·53	2·69
Copper	Cu	1083	8·9	0·092	16·6	0·94	1·55
Iron	Fe	1533	7·9	0·109	11·7	0·18	9·71
Lead	Pb	327	11·3	0·031	29·1	0·08	20·60
Magnesium	Mg	650	1·7	0·245	26·0	0·38	4·4
Nickel	Ni	1455	8·9	0·105	12·8	0·151	6·84
Silver	Ag	961	10·5	0·056	18·9	1·00	1·6
Tin	Sn	232	7·3	0·054	21·4	0·16	12·8
Zinc	Zn	419	7·1	0·092	33·0	0·27	5·9

1. The Structure of Metals

A knowledge of the structure of metals, however elementary, is essential for the fuller understanding of the subject of Engineering Metallurgy.

If a pure metal is melted, and the temperature recorded at various intervals during cooling, the cooling curve for that metal is obtained (Fig. 1.1). The horizontal portion of the curve is due to the evolution of latent heat at the freezing point.

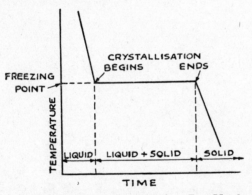

Fig. 1.1. The Cooling Curve for a Pure Metal

In the liquid state the atoms of a metal are haphazardly arranged but upon solidification they take up fixed positions in a regular pattern, referred to as a *space lattice*. This change which occurs at the freezing point is known as crystallization.

The common metals crystallize in one of three main types of metallic space lattice, namely, face-centred cubic, body-centred cubic or hexagonal close-packed. These are shown in Fig. 1.2 and represent the smallest unit of the crystalline metallic structure.

1

The crystalline structure, with its definite planes along which deformation can more readily occur, accounts for the characteristic metallic properties of ductility and malleability.

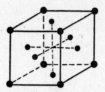

FACE CENTRED
CUBIC LATTICE.

Examples
Copper
Aluminium
Gamma Iron
Nickel

BODY CENTRED
CUBIC LATTICE.

Alpha Iron
Tungsten
Chromium
Molybdenum

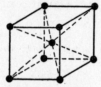

HEXAGONAL CLOSE-
PACKED LATTICE.

Zinc
Magnesium
Titanium
Cadmium

Fig. 1.2. The Main Types of Metallic
Space Lattice Arrangements of Atoms

THE MECHANISM OF CRYSTALLIZATION

Fig. 1.3. Solidifica-
tion of Metal Around
a Nucleus

Solidification or crystallization commences by the formation of small 'nuclei' scattered at random in the cooling liquid. At these points a few atoms assume an orderly arrangement to give, for example, the unit cubic structure, and growth occurs in three dimensions as represented in Fig. 1.3.

From the main arms of the crystal, secondary growths occur to give a crystal skeleton known as a dendrite.

2

Microscopic examination of a pure metal reveals a polygonal grain structure and the formation of these grains from the nuclei by dendritic growth is illustrated in Fig. 1.4.

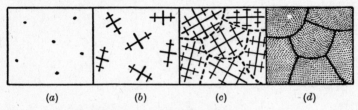

Fig. 1.4. Formation of Grains by Dendritic Growth
    (a) The formation of nuclei in the cooling liquid.
    (b) Dendritic crystals grow outwards from nuclei.
    (c) The dendritic arms meet. Growth outwards is impeded. The contact surface forms grain boundary.
    (d) The liquid between the arms of the dendrites solidifies giving homogeneous grains with no evidence of dendritic growth.

Each of these grains or crystals is built up of thousands of small unit cubes or cells. In each grain the axes of the cubes all point in the same direction, but this direction varies from one crystal to another, as shown in Fig. 1.5. This effect is known as the orientation of the atoms.

Fig. 1.5. Orientation of Atoms in Each Grain

THE GRAIN BOUNDARY

Since the orientation of the atoms in each grain is different it is obvious that the atoms of the metal at the grain boundary cannot be arranged on a regular space lattice. It is thought that a transition lattice exists at the grain boundary joining the regular cubic lattice of one grain to that of the other. Since the grain boundary structure is different from that of the grains, the properties will also be different.

Reference to Fig. 1.6 will show that at relatively low temperatures the grain boundaries are stronger than the grains, whereas at elevated temperatures the grain boundaries are weaker. It follows that a fine grained structure will give higher strength and hardness at room temperatures, but at higher temperatures a coarse grain would be preferred. These remarks apply to pure metals and solid solution alloys and may not apply to certain alloys with grain boundary impurities. The diagram also explains why, other things

3

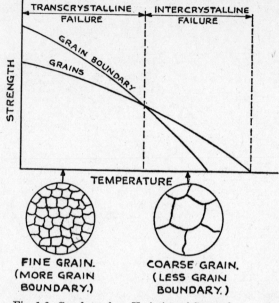

Fig. 1.6. Graph to show Variation of Strength
of Grains and Grain Boundaries with Temperature

being equal, the type of fracture at room temperatures is usually
transcrystalline (across the grain) whereas at elevated temperatures
fractures may be intercrystalline (along the grain boundaries)
(Fig. 1.7).

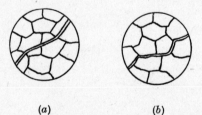

(a)   (b)

Fig. 1.7. Diagrammatic Representation of
(a) Transcrystalline Fracture
(b) Intercrystalline Fracture

It is apparent that the properties of a metal will be governed to
a large extent by the amount of grain boundary, i.e. the GRAIN
SIZE. The control of grain size is therefore very important in the
working and heat-treatment of metals and alloys.

4

THE CRYSTAL STRUCTURE OF INGOTS AND CASTINGS

Molten metal from the furnace is usually cast into metal moulds or sand moulds. The rate of cooling of the liquid metal is greater in the former and this increases the number of nuclei formed. Since each nucleus forms a grain, a finer grain size is obtained than in a sand casting.

In addition to the type of mould used the following factors are also important in controlling the grain size of cast metals.

1. Casting Temperature (Fig. 1.8). When the liquid metal makes contact with the cold metal mould a thin layer of chill crystals is formed. Long columnar crystals then grow towards the centre of the ingot from each face. If the casting temperature is too high these crystals will meet to form planes of weakness. However, if the casting temperature is correct, the liquid at the centre of the ingot will have solidified to give equiaxed grains before the columnar crystals can meet.

2. Section Thickness. Thin sections will cool more quickly and consequently a finer grain size is obtained compared with the thicker sections of a casting.

3. Purity of the Metal. In general the purer the metal the coarser the grain.

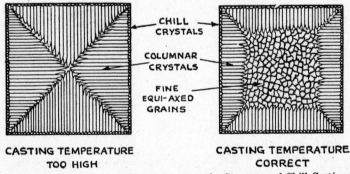

CHILL CRYSTALS

COLUMNAR CRYSTALS

FINE EQUI-AXED GRAINS

CASTING TEMPERATURE TOO HIGH

CASTING TEMPERATURE CORRECT

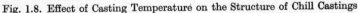

Fig. 1.8. Effect of Casting Temperature on the Structure of Chill Castings

The cast structure with its directional crystal growth is relatively weak, but as indicated later, the structure can be refined by subsequent working operations with consequent improvement in mechanical properties.

2. The Deformation and Annealing of Metals

THE COLD-WORKING OF METALS

Cold-working, e.g. rolling, drawing or pressing, is usually carried out on previously hot-worked metals and alloys. It is frequently the finishing stage in production. The effect of cold-working is to break down the crystal structure, elongating the grains in the direction of working (Fig. 2.1).

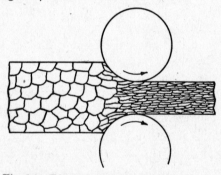

Fig. 2.1. Diagrammatic Representation of Changes occurring during Cold-working

Cold-work destroys the lattice structure with its regular crystal planes along which deformation can readily occur. The metal thus becomes harder and the characteristic ductility is lost. Hardening due to cold-working is referred to as WORK-HARDENING and is the only method available for increasing the hardness of pure metals and many non-ferrous alloys.

The advantages of cold-working over hot-working are:
1. More accurate control of dimensions
2. The production of a clean, bright finish
3. Improvement in yield point, hardness and machinability

6

THE ANNEALING OF COLD-WORKED METAL

Before further forming processes, e.g. pressing or deep drawing, can be carried out on cold-worked metal it is necessary to soften the material. This is achieved by annealing, which involves reheating the metal, when the following changes occur (Fig. 2.2):

(i) stress relief (ii) recrystallization (iii) grain growth

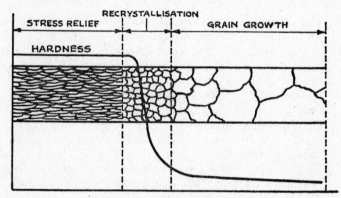

Fig. 2.2. Effect of Annealing Temperature on the Structure and Hardness of Cold-worked Metals

Stress Relief

At relatively low temperatures depending upon the particular metal or alloy the internal stresses induced by cold-working are removed. There is little change in hardness or microstructure during this stage. In some cases hardness and strength may actually increase slightly.

Recrystallization

When a certain temperature is reached the distorted grains are replaced by new fine polygonal grains and softening occurs. This phenomenon is known as recrystallization. The recrystallization temperature for a particular metal or alloy will depend upon a number of factors, namely:

(a) **The degree of prior cold-work.**
　　The greater the amount of prior deformation the lower the recrystallization temperature (Fig. 2.3).

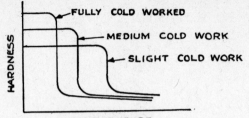

Fig. 2.3. Effect of Cold-working on Softening Temperature

(b) The addition of other elements.

Added elements generally raise the recrystallization temperature. Pure copper recrystallizes at 200°C., whilst the addition of 0·25% tin raises the recrystallization temperature to above 375°C. It follows that alloys generally recrystallize at higher temperatures than the metals from which they are composed.

(c) The annealing time.

Increasing time of annealing displaces recrystallization to a lower temperature.

The approximate recrystallization temperatures of some commercially pure fully cold-worked metals is shown in Table 2.1.

It will be noticed that certain metals, e.g. zinc, lead, tin, recrystallize at room temperatures; therefore these metals cannot be work-hardened since recrystallization occurs simultaneously with deformation.

Metal	Approx. Recrystallization temperature °C.	Melting Point °C.
Nickel	600	1455
Iron	450	1533
Copper	200	1083
Aluminium	150	660
Magnesium	150	651
Zinc	Room temp.	419
Lead	,, ,,	327
Tin	,, ,,	232

Table 2.1. Table to illustrate melting points and approximate recrystallization temperatures of some fully cold-worked metals

Grain Growth

If the annealing temperature is further increased the recrystallized grains grow in size. The new strain-free grains grow by absorbing others which are less stable. The two processes of recrystallization and grain growth are inseparable but it is more convenient to study them separately.

The factors governing grain growth are as follows:

(a) The annealing temperature and time (Fig. 2.4).

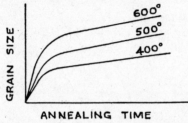

Fig. 2.4. Effect of Annealing Temperature
and Time on Grain Size

Reference to Fig. 2.4 indicates that the higher the annealing temperature the coarser the grain size. Grain growth is rapid at first and then becomes much slower.

(b) The degree of previous cold-work.

In general the greater the amount of cold-work the finer the grain size after complete recrystallization. In certain cases, a slight amount of deformation may give rise to an extremely large grain after recrystallization (Fig. 2.5). This critical amount of deformation due to cold-work varies according to the metal, being about 10% for iron. In this case deformation is defined as the percentage reduction in thickness or diameter due to cold-working.

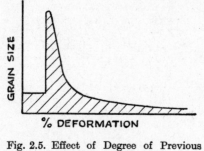
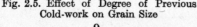

Fig. 2.5. Effect of Degree of Previous
Cold-work on Grain Size

9

(c) The presence of insoluble impurities.

These tend to prevent grain growth.

The annealing temperature and time should be closely controlled to avoid grain growth. A coarse grain produces a roughened surface ('orange peel' effect) in subsequent pressing operations. A coarse-grained alloy cannot be remedied by further heat-treatment. Recrystallization after cold-work is the only method of grain refinement available for most non-ferrous metals and alloys.

HOT-WORKING

The distinction between hot-working and cold-working is that the former takes place above the recrystallization temperature (or lower critical range for steel). In hot-working, deformation and recrystallization occur simultaneously (Fig. 2.6) so that the rate of softening is greater than the rate of work-hardening.

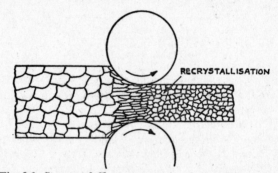

Fig. 2.6. Structural Changes occurring during Hot-working

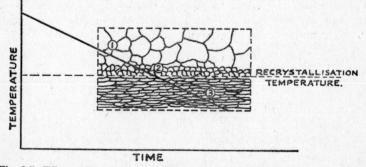

Fig. 2.7. Effect of Finishing Temperature on the Structure of Hot-worked Metal

1.	Finishing temperature too high		Coarse grain
2.	,, ,,	correct	Fine grain
3.	,, ,,	too low	Distorted grain
			Work hardening

10

The important factor in hot-working is the finishing temperature. This is apparent from Fig. 2.7. Hot-working should be finished at a temperature just above the recrystallization temperature so that a fine grain size is obtained. If the finishing temperature is too high then grain growth will occur whilst the metal is cooling above the recrystallization temperature. If on the other hand the finishing temperature is too low then work-hardening will result.

Far less power is required to deform metals at high temperatures since the metal is usually softer and more plastic. Hot-working is therefore more economical. The chief processes of hot-working are hot-rolling, forging and extrusion. In general, simple shapes, e.g. sheet, plate, rod, are usually hot-rolled, whilst the more complicated shapes are forged. Non-ferrous sections and tubes are usually made by extrusion.

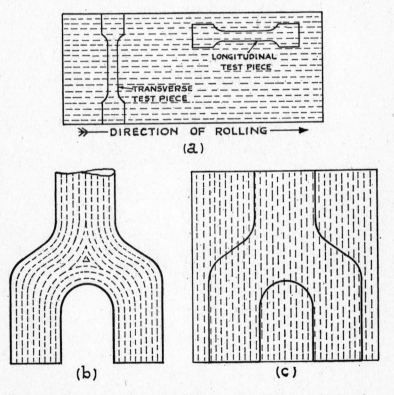

Fig. 2.8. Effect of Direction of Working or 'Fibre' on Mechanical Properties

EFFECTS OF HOT-WORKING

1. The ingot structure, with its coarse columnar crystals, is destroyed.

2. If the finishing temperature is correct, grain refinement is obtained.

3. The non-metallic inclusions are elongated into fibres, thus indicating the flow of the metal.

4. In certain cases, e.g. with rimming steels (page 27), internal blowholes may be welded up.

5. Strength, ductility and toughness are improved but directional properties are produced. The improvement is greater in the direction of working than in the transverse direction (Fig. 2.8(a)).

In forgings, the 'fibre' or flow lines should follow the contour of the section (Fig. 2.8(b)). Forgings are, therefore, superior in mechanical properties to similar shapes machined from hot-rolled material (Fig. 2.8(c)).

3. Thermal Equilibrium Diagrams

Pure metals are often too soft and weak for many commercial applications and consequently alloys are more widely used as engineering materials. For example, steel (an alloy of iron and carbon) is stronger than pure iron and can also be heat-treated to produce desirable mechanical properties. Alloy systems can best be studied with reference to constitutional or equilibrium diagrams. These diagrams are really temperature-composition diagrams which indicate the structural changes that take place during the heating and cooling of an alloy. Although they only refer to equilibrium conditions, which are rarely obtained in practice, they form a useful basis for the study of the treatment and properties of alloys.

Alloys containing two metals are referred to as binary alloys. Even when more than two metals are present, much useful information can be obtained by the study of the binary diagram for the two principal metals. The constituent metals in most commercial binary alloys are soluble in each other in the liquid state. Assuming that they do not combine to form a compound, binary alloys can be divided into three types, namely:

(a) The two metals are completely insoluble in each other in the solid state (*simple eutectic type*).

(b) The two metals are completely soluble in each other in the solid state (*solid-solution type*).

(c) The two metals are partially soluble in each other in the solid state (*combination type*).

Each of these types gives rise to a characteristic equilibrium diagram which may be recognized at a glance. These are illustrated in Fig. 3.1.

In certain cases a peritectic reaction may occur during solidification. The meaning of this and other terms will be explained later,

13

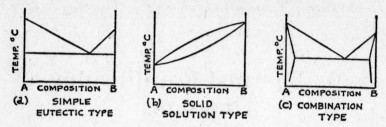

Fig. 3.1. Characteristic Types of Binary Equilibrium Diagrams for Alloys
of the Metals A and B

but here again a characteristic type of diagram may be recognized
(Fig. 3.2).

The equilibrium diagrams for the chief engineering alloys, e.g.
steels (Fe-C), brasses (Cu-Zn), bronzes (Cu-Sn), etc., are all complex
diagrams, but they can be interpreted on the basis of the simple

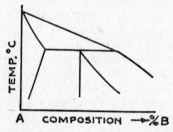

Fig. 3.2. Part of Equilibrium Diagram of a Binary Series of Alloys
involving a Peritectic Reaction

types mentioned above, viz. eutectic, solid solution and peritectic.
It is therefore essential to understand these basic diagrams before
proceeding to study commercial alloy systems.

COOLING CURVES FOR BINARY ALLOYS

The cooling curve for a pure metal is shown in Fig. 1.1. It will be
noticed that freezing takes place at a constant temperature. However, with the exception of alloys of exact eutectic composition,
alloys freeze over a range of temperature, as indicated in Fig. 3.3.

The points A and B denote the temperatures corresponding to
the beginning and end of freezing, and are known as the first and

second arrest points respectively. In Fig. 3.3(*a*) it will be observed that solidification finally occurs at a constant temperature and this is true for all alloys which form a eutectic.

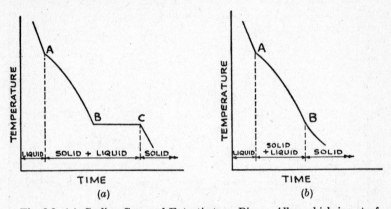

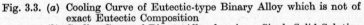

Fig. 3.3. (*a*) Cooling Curve of Eutectic-type Binary Alloy which is not of exact Eutectic Composition
(*b*) Cooling Curve of Binary Alloy forming a Single Solid Solution

THE CONSTRUCTION OF THERMAL EQUILIBRIUM DIAGRAMS
e.g. The Simple Eutectic Type

Equilibrium diagrams may be constructed using the information supplied from the cooling curves of a number of alloys of the two metals concerned.

The upper diagram in Fig. 3.4 represents a series of cooling curves obtained using various alloys of the two metals A and B. The first curve refers to pure metal A, the other curves to alloys containing (80% A 20% B), (60% A 40% B), (40% A 60% B), (20% A 80% B), while the last curve is that for pure metal B. By joining the first arrest points (represented by circles) we obtain the liquidus curves, above which the alloys are entirely liquid. By joining the second arrest points (represented by crosses) we obtain the solidus line, below which the alloys are entirely solid. Between the solidus and the liquidus the alloy is a paste of part solid and part liquid.

It is apparent from Fig. 3.4 that by increasing the proportion of metal B to metal A the freezing point has been lowered as shown by curve AC. Similarly curve BC shows the effect of increasing the proportion of metal A to metal B. At C, the point of intersection, we have an alloy with the lowest freezing point in the series. This alloy is known as the *eutectic*, the word being derived from the Greek

15

meaning 'easy melting'. At the eutectic temperature both metal A and metal B will crystallize simultaneously at a constant temperature. Eutectics usually possess a laminated structure, consisting of alternate laminations of the two constituents. In this example we

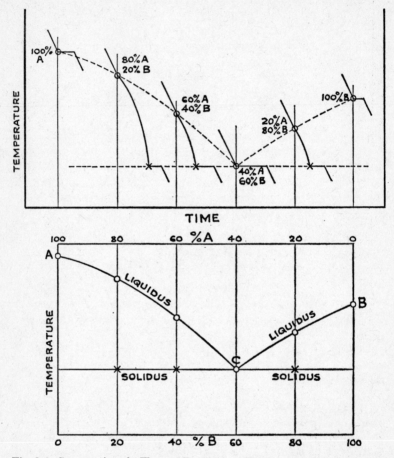

Fig. 3.4. Construction of a Thermal Equilibrium Diagram from Cooling Curves

have a eutectic of two pure metals, but eutectics may consist of solid solutions, or chemical compounds. A comprehensive definition of a eutectic is as follows:

A eutectic consists of two or more solid phases produced by solidification at constant temperature. It is the alloy of the lowest freezing point (melting point) in the series.

16

THE INTERPRETATION OF THE SIMPLE EUTECTIC DIAGRAM

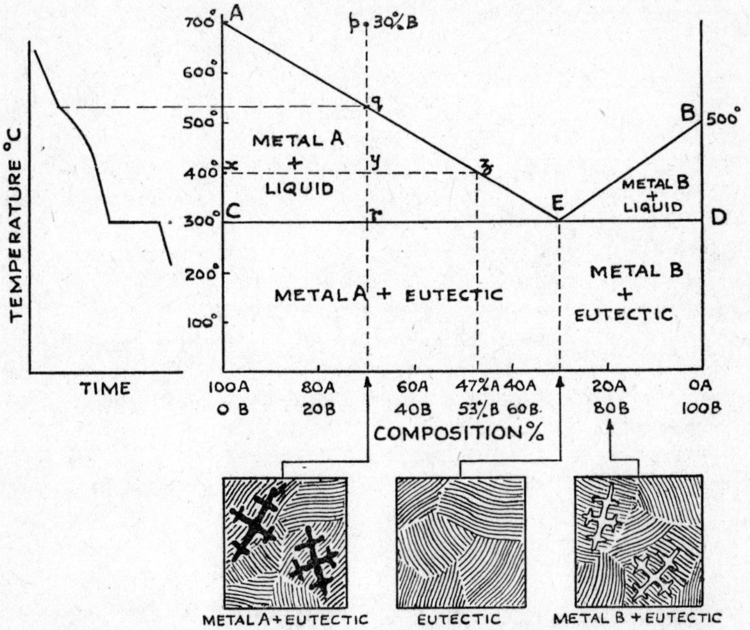

Fig. 3.5. Thermal Equilibrium Diagram of the Simple Eutectic Type

Let us consider a hypothetical simple eutectic diagram of two metals A and B. Metal A melts at 700°C. and metal B at 500°C. They form a eutectic containing 70% B 30% A which melts at 300°C.

Consider the cooling of an alloy containing 30% B. The alloy contains more of metal A than required to form a eutectic. Upon reaching point q on the liquidus (approximately 525°C.) crystals of metal A will be formed. As the temperature decreases more crystals of metal A are deposited and the liquid becomes progressively richer in metal B, as represented by the liquidus qE.

At 400°C. the alloy will consist of solid metal A plus liquid of composition z (53% B 47% A). The relative weights of solid and liquid are given by the relative lengths of the lines yz and xy.

$$\frac{\text{Weight of solid}}{\text{Weight of liquid}} = \frac{yz}{xy} = \frac{23}{30}$$

Upon reaching point r (300°C.) the liquid has attained the eutectic

17

composition E (70% B 30% A). At this temperature, both metals A and B will crystallize simultaneously to form the eutectic structure. No further changes will occur upon cooling to room temperatures. The final microstructure will therefore consist of dendrites of metal A plus eutectic. All the alloys containing up to 70% B will consist of these two phases, but the proportion of eutectic will increase with increasing content of metal B.

Alloys with greater than 70% B will commence to solidify by depositing metal B. The residual liquid will become progressively richer in metal A as the temperature falls until it reaches a composition of 30% A 70% B at 300°C. At this temperature both metals will crystallize simultaneously as eutectic.

The alloy of composition E will solidify entirely as eutectic at a constant temperature (300°C.).

It will be apparent that microscopic examination can be used to estimate the composition of an alloy. For example if examination revealed approximately equal proportions of metal A and eutectic the composition would be mid-way between 0 and 70% B, giving a composition of 35% B 65% A.

Examples of alloy systems which give rise to simple eutectic diagrams are the bismuth-cadmium and zinc-tin alloys. However, most metals usually have a slight solid solubility and the combination type of diagram is more common than the simple eutectic.

EUTECTOID

At this stage it is convenient to define the term 'eutectoid' which is closely related to a eutectic. A eutectoid consists of two or more solid phases produced by the breakdown of a solid solution at constant temperature, whereas a eutectic is formed by solidification. Examples of eutectoid formation will be discussed when considering the steels, tin bronzes, and aluminium bronzes.

SOLID-SOLUTION ALLOYS

In certain alloys the complete solubility that exists in the liquid state persists after solidification. The solid alloy, known as a solid solution, consists of one kind of crystal lattice structure in which both metals are present. However, if the alloy is examined microscopically it is impossible to trace the two constituent metals, since a single-phase structure exists.

There are two types of solid-solution alloy, namely substitutional and interstitial.

(a) *Substitutional Solid Solutions*

The atoms of the added metal can be substituted for those of the parent metal on the lattice. In such cases the metals must possess nearly equal atomic diameters. Copper and nickel are mutually soluble in all proportions to form substitutional solid solutions (Fig. 3.6).

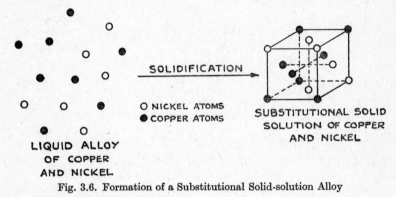

Fig. 3.6. Formation of a Substitutional Solid-solution Alloy

(b) *Interstitial Solid Solutions*

The atoms of the added elements enter the interstices of the parent lattice. In other words, they fit into the spaces between the atoms of the parent metal. This is of less common occurrence and is only possible if the atoms of the added element are small compared with those of the parent metal. A good example is that of carbon in iron to form the various steel solid solutions (Fig. 3.7).

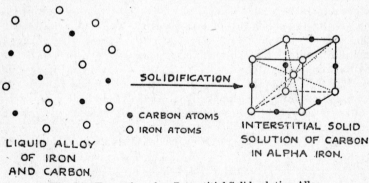

Fig. 3.7. Formation of an Interstitial Solid-solution Alloy

In certain alloys containing three metals, known as ternary alloys, both types of solid solution may co-exist. For example, in austenitic manganese steel there is a substitutional solid solution of manganese and iron and also an interstitial solid solution of carbon in iron.

THE SOLID-SOLUTION DIAGRAM

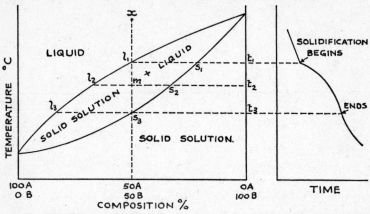

Fig. 3.8. Thermal Equilibrium Diagram of the Solid-solution Type

This diagram may be constructed in a manner similar to that used for the simple eutectic type, namely by joining the first and second arrest points obtained from a series of cooling curves of alloys in the system.

A typical solid solution type of diagram is shown in Fig. 3.8. The upper curve is the liquidus and the lower curve the solidus.

Consider the cooling of an alloy of composition x, containing equal amounts of the two metals A and B. Solidification commences at t_1 when a solid solution of composition s_1 (richer in metal B than 50%) is deposited. Solidification proceeds by the absorption of metal A from the liquid which diffuses throughout the solid. Hence as the temperature falls from t_1 to t_3, the solid solution changes its composition along the solidus $s_1 s_3$ whilst the liquid changes its composition along the liquidus $l_1 l_3$. At t_3 the alloy is completely solid and consists of uniform grains of solid solution of composition s_3, the last drop of liquid having the composition l_3.

At some intermediate temperature t_2 we have a solid solution of composition s_2 in equilibrium with a liquid solution of composition l_2. The relative weights of solid and liquid are given by the relative lengths of the lines l_2m and s_2m.

$$\frac{\text{Weight of solid solution } s_2}{\text{Weight of liquid solution } l_2} = \frac{l_2m}{s_2m}$$

20

Effect of Cooling Rate

It has been seen that the initial dendritic deposits are richer in metal B whilst the last liquid to solidify was richer in metal A. With slow cooling rates diffusion has time to occur producing a structure consisting of a single constituent or phase, similar to that of a pure metal. However, in practice, the cooling rate is too rapid to allow diffusion to occur and what is known as a CORED structure results (Fig. 3.9). Coring can be eliminated by annealing, when diffusion of

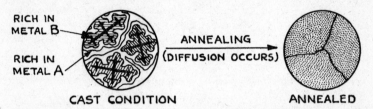

Fig. 3.9. Effect of Annealing on the Microstructure of a Cast Solid-solution Alloy

the two metals occurs. Examples of binary solid-solution alloys are copper-nickel, bismuth-antimony and gold-silver.

THE COMBINATION-TYPE DIAGRAM

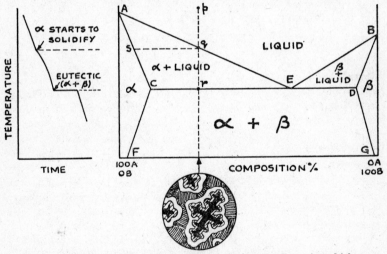

Fig. 3.10. Equilibrium Diagram for Binary Series of Alloys in which two Metals are partially Soluble in each other in the Solid State

This type of equilibrium diagram (Fig. 3.10) is really a combination of the two previous types. The liquidus line AEB is similar to that of the simple eutectic diagram. The solidus line in this diagram is ACEDB and contains two parts, namely, AC and BD which are similar to the solidus line on the solid solution diagram.

The solid solubility of B in A and A in B increases with temperature, as shown by the lines FC and GD respectively. The maximum solubility is reached at the eutectic temperature, when the compositions of the two solid solutions α and β are denoted by the points C and D respectively. In this case the eutectic of composition E consists of the two solid solutions α and β.

Consider the cooling of an alloy of composition p. Solidification commences on reaching point q on the liquidus line when solid solution α of composition s is deposited. When the temperature falls to that of the eutectic, the alloy will now consist of α of composition C and liquid of composition E. The liquid will solidify completely to form a eutectic of the two solid solutions α and β in the proportions $\alpha:\beta = \text{ED}:\text{CE}$. Upon further cooling the α and β in the eutectic will become poorer in metals B and A respectively. Their compositions at room temperature are represented by F and G respectively. The primary dendrites of α solid solution will also become poorer in metal B, changing in composition along CF, and this will precipitate a small amount of β solid solution, which will be associated with the eutectic.

Examples of binary alloy systems of this type are the lead-tin, copper-silver and bismuth-tin alloys.

PERITECTIC REACTIONS

During the freezing of certain alloys the solid already deposited may react with the residual liquid to form another solid solution or compound of a composition intermediate between that of the first solid and the liquid. This reaction occurs at constant temperature, and the alloy is said to undergo a peritectic transformation.

A peritectic reaction gives rise to a characteristic type of diagram as shown in Fig. 3.11. Consider the cooling of an alloy of composition p. Solidification commences at t_1 when crystals of solid solution α of composition s are deposited. Throughout the temperature range t_1–t_3 the composition of the α varies along the solidus line AB whilst the liquid varies in composition along the liquidus line AD. At t_3 there exists α of composition B in equilibrium with liquid of composition D in the ratio qD:qB. The peritectic reaction occurs at this temperature when α solid solution of composition B reacts with liquid of composition D to form a new solid solution β of composition C. Since the original liquid is not rich enough in metal B to form entirely β solid solution, some α solid solution remains unchanged. The alloy solidifies at this temperature leaving a structure of α and β of composition B and C respectively. Although the two solid solutions vary in composition on cooling, the general structure still remains the same.

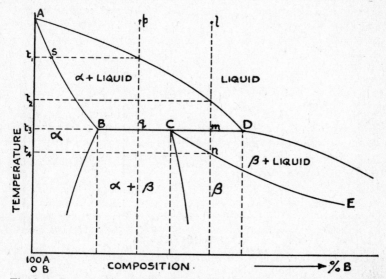

Fig. 3.11. Part of a Binary-alloy Diagram in which a Solid Solution is formed by a Peritectic Reaction

The alloy of composition l contains more of metal B than that required to form the β solid solution. This alloy begins to solidify at t_2, and at t_3 will consist of solid solution α of composition B and liquid solution of composition D in the ratio of mD:mB. The peritectic reaction occurs at this temperature and will proceed until all the α solid solution has transformed, leaving β solid solution + liquid. Upon further cooling the β changes in composition along the solidus CE, being completely solid at temperature t_4 when it consists of uniform crystals of composition l.

Examples of binary systems involving a peritectic reaction are iron-carbon, copper-zinc and copper-tin.

INTERMETALLIC COMPOUNDS

In some alloy systems the two metals may enter into definite chemical combination. The compound produced, known as an *intermetallic compound*, is apparent under the microscope, frequently as definite rectangular particles. The existence of a compound which

c   23

has a definite melting point is indicated by a maximum in the liquidus curve (Fig. 3.12).

The diagram may be considered as two eutectic diagrams placed together. In the example shown, the compound and each metal are completely insoluble in the solid state. Examples of alloy systems in which an intermetallic compound is formed are magnesium-zinc and magnesium-tin.

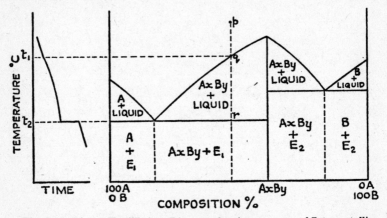

Fig. 3.12. Binary Equilibrium Diagram showing presence of Intermetallic Compound
E_1 = Eutectic of $(Ax\,By + A)$
E_2 = Eutectic of $(Ax\,By + B)$

Consider the cooling of an alloy of composition p. Solidification commences at temperature t_1, represented by point q on the liquidus, when crystals of the compound $Ax\,By$ are deposited. Upon further cooling the liquid becomes progressively richer in metal A until at temperature t_2, represented by point r on the solidus, it has reached the eutectic composition E. At this temperature, both metal A and the compound $Ax\,By$ solidify simultaneously as a eutectic at constant temperature. The final structure will therefore consist of primary crystals of the compound $Ax\,By$ in a eutectic matrix.

24

4. Plain Carbon Steels

BRIEF OUTLINE OF STEEL MAKING

Steel making involves the removal, by oxidation, of the impurities from pig iron or a mixture of pig iron and steel scrap. Pig iron contains 3–4% carbon, together with smaller amounts of manganese, silicon, sulphur, and phosphorus. These elements make the iron weak and brittle and their partial removal is necessary to produce a stronger and more ductile product for commercial use. The chief processes available are the open-hearth and the Bessemer. The electric-arc process is also used for making high-grade alloy steels, usually from a charge of scrap steel, although a certain amount of refining is involved.

Steel-making processes are usually classified as either 'acid' or 'basic'. These terms refer to the type of furnace lining and consequently the nature of the slag. In the acid process the furnace lining consists usually of silica. However, in order to remove phosphorus from pig iron it is necessary to add lime, resulting in a basic slag. Because this slag reacts with the acid silica lining, acid processes are unsuitable for treating the pig irons produced from high phosphorus ores. Such pig irons can only be treated in a basic process using magnesite or dolomite as furnace lining. Magnesite consists of magnesium carbonate $MgCO_3$, whereas dolomite is essentially a mixture of the carbonates of calcium and magnesium. $CaCO_3$. $MgCO_3$. At one time basic steel was regarded as inferior to acid steel, but with present techniques basic steel is just as good. A comparison of the two types of processes is shown in Table 4.1.

DEOXIDATION

At the end of the steel-making process some iron will be in the oxidized condition and deoxidation is necessary before pouring the

25

steel into ingot moulds. Deoxidizers, such as ferro-manganese, ferro-silicon and aluminium, are added at the end of the process to remove this soluble iron oxide. These additions have a strong affinity for oxygen and form insoluble oxides of manganese, silicon or aluminium. These insoluble oxides normally enter the slag, but if they do not they will form non-metallic inclusions in the steel.

	Acid	*Basic*
Refractory lining	Silica	Magnesite
Composition of pig iron used	High silicon Low phosphorus	High phosphorus Low silicon
Slag	Acid (high silica)	Basic (high lime)
Elements removed by oxidation	C, Si, Mn	C, Si, Mn, P, S

Table 4.1. Comparison of Acid and Basic Steel-making Processes

Normally such inclusions are not too detrimental. If they are soft they can be readily elongated in the direction of working, giving rise to 'fibre' and directional properties (Fig. 2.8). However, hard inclusions, such as the oxide of aluminium (Al_2O_3), are not elongated and act as points of stress concentration. These inclusions give rise to low Izod impact test values, corrosion fatigue, poor machinability and excessive tool wear. They also cause increased abrasion of dies in wire drawing, as well as causing the steel wire to have a very poor surface.

KILLED AND RIMMING STEELS

Steels that have been completely deoxidized are referred to as 'killed' steels. Such steels are free from blow holes and are characterized by 'piping', a term used to describe the normal solidification shrinkage cavity. This can be minimized by using a wide-end up mould together with a refractory 'hot top' or feeder head (Fig. 4.1). Rimming steels are cast in an oxidized condition, deoxidation not being complete. The control of deoxidation is very important in the manufacture of rimming steels. A thick rim of pure metal solidifies and the residual liquid is enriched sufficiently in carbon to react with the oxide.

$$FeO + C = Fe + CO$$

The carbon monoxide CO evolved causes a risen surface which counteracts the piping and gives rise to a core which contains numerous blow holes (Fig. 4.1(b)). Rimming steels are usually low

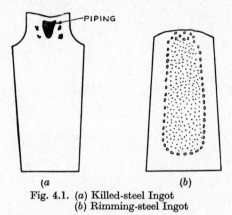

(a)   (b)

Fig. 4.1. (a) Killed-steel Ingot
(b) Rimming-steel Ingot

carbon steels, especially suitable for sheet and plate, due to their pure rim. Since the carbon content is low the internal blow holes are welded up during subsequent hot rolling.

STRUCTURE OF PLAIN CARBON STEELS

Allotropy of Pure Iron

Before studying the structure of plain carbon steels it is essential to understand the structural changes that occur during the heating and cooling of pure iron itself. Pure iron exhibits allotropy, which may be defined as the phenomenon of an element existing in more than one physical form. This can be seen by plotting the volume of the unit cell of pure iron against the temperature (Fig. 4.2). A crystal structure exists in the temperature range 937°–1,400°C different from that at other temperatures. This is the allotropic form known as γ iron and possesses a face-centred cubic lattice. At the other temperatures a body-centred cubic lattice exists, this being the crystal structure of α, β and δ iron. The change points (or critical points) denoting the changes α–β, β–γ, γ–δ, are referred to as the A_2, A_3 and A_4 points respectively. The A_2 change point at 769°C. is the temperature at which iron loses its magnetism and is not important in heat-treatment work. In steels there is an additional change point, known as the A_1 point, which is associated with the formation of the eutectoid pearlite.

These structural changes in the solid state involve the evolution

27

of heat and may be studied with reference to an *inverse-rate* cooling curve. Such curves are more sensitive than direct cooling curves in detecting the smaller heat changes that occur in solid-state transformations. Inverse-rate curves are obtained by plotting the

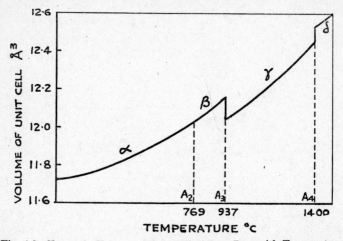

Fig. 4.2. Change in Volume of Unit Cell of Pure Iron with Temperature

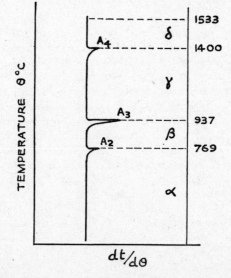

Fig. 4.3. Inverse-rate Cooling Curve for Pure Iron

28

temperature θ against $\dfrac{dt}{d\theta}$ where t represents the time. The thermal effect accompanying the phase change is prominent as a peak on the curve. The temperatures given for these various change points are those obtained upon heating the iron. Upon cooling it is noticed that they occur at somewhat lower temperatures. The change points obtained upon heating and cooling are referred to as Ac and Ar points respectively. For example, the Ac_1 and Ar_1 points occur at 730°C. and 695°C. respectively, whilst the Ac_3 and Ar_3 occur at 937°C. and 910°C. respectively.

THE 'STEEL PORTION' OF THE IRON-CARBON DIAGRAM

By joining the upper critical points (A_3) and the lower critical points (A_1) obtained from a series of inverse-rate cooling curves using steels of varying carbon contents, the steel portion of the iron-carbon diagram may be constructed (Fig. 4.4). For the purpose of this discussion the term 'steel portion' refers to that part of the iron-carbon diagram of use in the heat treatment of plain carbon steels. It will be noticed that the addition of carbon lowers the A_3 point until at 0·83% carbon it merges with the A_1 point. This is the eutectoid point at 695°C. and is associated with the formation of the structure known as pearlite.

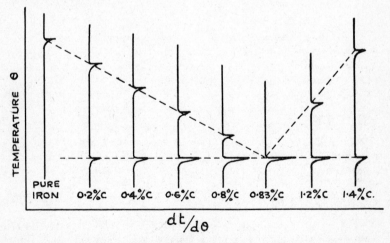

Fig. 4.4. Construction of 'Steel Portion' of Iron-carbon Diagram from Inverse-rate Cooling Curves

The 'steel portion' of the iron-carbon diagram is shown in Fig. 4.5.

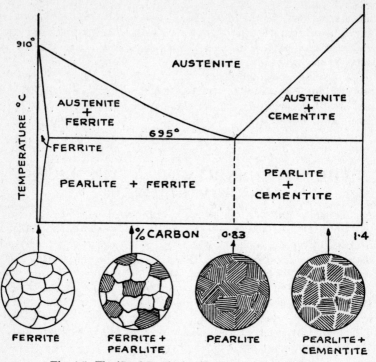

Fig. 4.5. The 'Steel Portion' of the Iron-carbon Diagram

Those steels with less than 0·83% carbon are referred to as hypo-eutectoid steels, whilst those with more than 0·83% are known as hyper-eutectoid steels. The various microconstituents present in plain carbon steels may be defined as follows:

FERRITE

A solid solution of carbon in body-centred cubic α iron, containing a maximum of 0·04% carbon at 695°C. It is soft, ductile and readily cold-worked.

CEMENTITE

A hard brittle compound of iron and carbon with the formula Fe_3C. This may exist in the free state usually as a grain boundary film, or as a constituent of the eutectoid pearlite.

PEARLITE

This is the eutectoid structure consisting of alternate laminations of ferrite and cementite. It contains 0·83% carbon and is formed by the breakdown of the austenite solid solution at 695°C.

AUSTENITE

A solid solution of carbon in face-centred cubic γ iron, containing a maximum of 1·7% carbon at 1,130°C. It is soft and non-magnetic, and only exists in plain carbon steels above the upper critical range. It may, however, occur at room temperatures in certain alloy steels.

MECHANICAL PROPERTIES OF PLAIN CARBON STEELS

The mechanical properties of slowly cooled plain carbon steels will depend upon the proportion of each of the microconstituents present. The mechanical properties vary linearly from 0% carbon (100% ferrite) to 0·83% carbon (100% pearlite). After 0·83% carbon, free cementite appears in the microstructure and the linear relationship exists no longer.

Using the values stated in Table 4.2 it is a simple matter to construct a graph such as that shown in Fig. 4.6. It is not practicable to carry out a tensile test on a specimen of cementite and hence the results given for this constituent are only estimated values.

Microconstituent	U.T.S. Tons/sq. in.	% Elongn.	B.H.N.
Ferrite	22	40	100
Cementite	3	nil	650
Pearlite	60	5	280

Table 4.2. The Mechanical Properties of the Constituents Present in Slowly Cooled Plain Carbon Steels

It should be emphasized that the properties obtained in normalizing (which involves air cooling) vary according to the thickness of section. Fully annealed steels (furnaced cooled) would give a softer and more ductile steel. A further limitation of the use Fig. 4.6 is that it does not take into account the effect of variation of other

31

elements present in plain carbon steels. With these limitations in mind, a simple empirical formula can be obtained from the slope of the U.T.S. curve in Fig. 4.6. This gives the relation between carbon

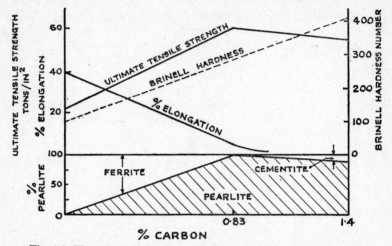

Fig. 4.6. The Effect of Carbon on the Microstructure and Mechanical Properties of Plain Carbon Steels in the Normalized Condition

content and ultimate tensile strength for a hypo-eutectoid normalized steel as,

$$y = 45x + 22$$
$$y = \text{U.T.S. in tons per square inch}$$
$$x = \text{carbon}\%$$

An empirical formula for estimating mechanical properties is not reliable, but provided its limitations are realized it provides a useful guide to the engineer.

RELATIONSHIP BETWEEN CARBON CONTENT AND MICROSTRUCTURE

It is evident that microscopic examination of slowly cooled plain carbon steels can be used to estimate the approximate carbon content. The following formula can be readily derived for hypo-eutectoid steels.

$$\%\text{Pearlite} = \frac{\%\text{ Carbon} \times 100}{0 \cdot 83}$$
$$\%\text{Ferrite} = \frac{(0 \cdot 83 - \%\text{Carbon}) \times 100}{0 \cdot 83}$$

32

EFFECT OF OTHER ELEMENTS PRESENT IN PLAIN CARBON STEELS

In addition to carbon, all plain carbon steels contain the following elements:

Manganese —up to 1%
Silicon — ,, ,, 0·3%
Sulphur — ,, ,, 0·05%
Phosphorus— ,, ,, 0·05%

The separate effects of each of these elements are:

Manganese

This is an essential constituent since it ensures freedom from blow holes and combines with the sulphur present (see note on effect of sulphur below). In general manganese raises the yield point, U.T.S. and impact test values. It increases the depth of hardening but also increases the tendency to distort or crack upon quench-hardening. For this reason the manganese content should be kept below 0·5% in medium and high-carbon steels, which have to be heat-treated in this manner.

Silicon

In most commercial mild steels the silicon content is of the order of 0·1–0·2%. In these amounts it has little direct effect on the mechanical properties. In high-carbon steels it should not exceed 0·2% since it assists the breakdown of cementite into ferrite and graphite.

Sulphur

Sulphur in steel may exist in two forms:
(a) As manganese sulphide inclusions.
    These are soft dove-grey inclusions which are readily elongated in the direction of working (Fig. 4.7(a)).
(b) As ferrous sulphide inclusions.
    These occur as a brown grain boundary film (Fig. 4.7(b)). It is hard and brittle and possesses a low melting point thereby giving rise to cracking during hot- and cold-working of the steel. In order to avoid the formation of ferrous sulphide inclusions a manganese:sulphur ratio of at least 5:1 is maintained in plain carbon steels.
In general the sulphur content should be kept below 0·05% but certain free-cutting steels contain about 0·2% of sulphur and

1·5% manganese. This ensures the formation of numerous manganese sulphide inclusions which aid machinability.

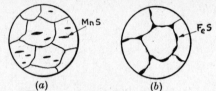

(a)   (b)

Fig. 4.7. (a) Manganese Sulphide Inclusions
(b) Ferrous Sulphide Inclusions at Grain Boundary

Phosphorus

Phosphorus has a pronounced tendency to segregate in steel. Hence the average composition should be kept below 0·05% to prevent the appearance of the brittle compound Fe_3P as a separate constituent.

CLASSIFICATION AND APPLICATIONS OF PLAIN CARBON STEELS (Table 4.3)

Carbon%	Type	Use
0·07–0·15	Dead Mild Steel	Cold-rolled strip for pressings, hot-rolled strip and bars. Rod and wire for nails, rivets and mattresses. Solid-drawn tubes.
0·15–0·30	Mild Steel	Case-hardening steels. Boiler and ship's plate; steel sections, e.g. joists, channels, angles.
0·3–0·6	Medium-Carbon Steel	Forgings for general engineering purposes. Connecting rods. Axles. Crankshafts. Fishplates.
0·6–0·8	High-Carbon Steel	Railway rails and tyres. Laminated springs. Wire ropes. Cast-steel die blocks. Band saws. Small forging dies.
0·8–1·4	Carbon Tool Steel	0·85–0·95% C. Small cold chisels. Shear blades. Punches. 0·95–1·1% C. Drills. Axes. Files. Hand saws. 1·1–1·4% C. Razors. Turning and planing tools. Drills.

THE COMPLETE IRON-CARBON DIAGRAM

The so-called complete iron-carbon diagram extends only to 6·68% carbon, which is the carbon content of cementite. The diagram is, therefore, more strictly the iron/iron carbide diagram. We have already considered the usefulness of the diagram in the study of steels. The diagram is also useful in the study of cast irons, which contain approximately 2·5–3·75% carbon. The structure and properties of cast irons will be discussed in Chapter 9.

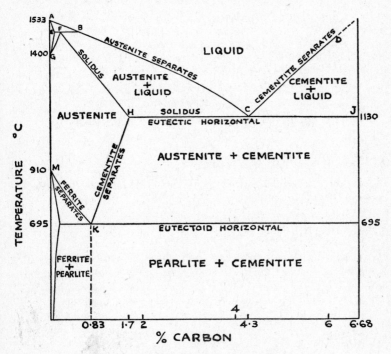

Fig. 4.8. The Complete Iron-carbon Diagram

The complete iron-carbon diagram may appear complicated at first sight, but may be considered as being made up of several simple basic diagrams, similar to those considered in Chapter 3. The main portions are as follows:

1. The Peritectic Portion (Fig. 4.9)

This occurs at 1,492°C. when δ solid solution containing 0·05%

carbon reacts with liquid containing 0·55% carbon to form a new solid solution, austenite, containing 0·18% carbon.

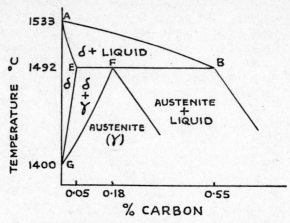

Fig. 4.9. The Peritectic Portion of the Iron-carbon Diagram (enlarged)

2. The Eutectic Portion

Liquid containing 4·3% carbon solidifies at 1,130°C. to form a eutectic consisting of austenite + cemenite.

3. The Solid-solution Portions

Two solid solutions are formed as previously mentioned on page 30. Austenite is a solid solution of carbon in γ iron, containing a maximum of 1·7% carbon at 1,130°C. Ferrite is a solid solution of carbon in α iron, containing a maximum of 0·04% carbon at 695°C.

4. The Eutectoid Portion

Austenite containing 0·83% carbon transforms at 695°C. to give a eutectoid consisting of ferrite and cementite, known as pearlite.

The lines MK and HK denote the beginning of the precipitation of ferrite and cementite respectively from austenite. The liquidus curves comprise AB, BC, and CD and the solidus curves AE, EF, FH, HC, and CJ.

5. Heat-treatment of Plain Carbon Steels

The mechanical properties of plain carbon steels can be varied considerably by heat-treatment. This is due to the structural changes which occur during the heating and cooling of such steels.

There are four conventional methods of heat-treatment:
1. Annealing
2. Normalizing
3. Hardening
4. Tempering

In addition there are processes such as Martempering and Austempering depending upon the constant temperature (isothermal) transformations of austenite. The heat-treatment ranges for plain carbon steels are shown in Fig. 5.1.

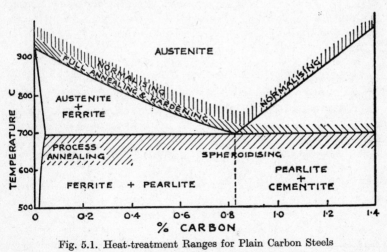

Fig. 5.1. Heat-treatment Ranges for Plain Carbon Steels

1. ANNEALING

Annealing is a general term applied to several softening operations, e.g. (a) process annealing, (b) full annealing, and (c) spheroidizing.

(a) Process Annealing

Process or sub-critical annealing is carried out on cold-worked low-carbon steel sheet or wire in order to relieve internal stress and to soften the material. The steel is heated to 550°–650°C., which is just below the lower critical range (Fig. 5.1).

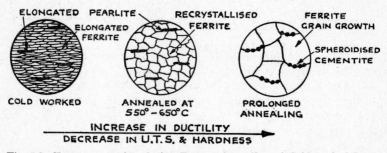

Fig. 5.2. Changes occurring during Process Annealing of Cold-worked Low-carbon Steel

The changes taking place during process annealing are represented in Fig. 5.2. This is an example of recrystallization annealing mentioned in Chapter 2. Prolonged annealing causes the cementite in the pearlite to 'ball up' or spheroidize. Ferrite grain growth also occurs and the annealing temperature and time should be closely controlled.

(b) Full Annealing

Full annealing is carried out on hot-worked and cast steels in order to obtain grain refinement in combination with high ductility. Compared with normalizing, it produces a softer steel with better machinability.

For hypo-eutectoid steels the treatment involves heating the steel to 30°–50°C. above the upper critical range, holding it at this temperature for a time depending on thickness, followed by slow cooling, usually in the furnace. For hyper-eutectoid steels the temperature is about 50°C. above the lower critical point.

If the temperature of annealing is not closely controlled, certain defects may occur, e.g. overheating, burning or under-annealing.

Overheating

If the steel is heated to above the correct annealing temperature, or if it is maintained too long at the annealing temperature, austenite grain-growth will occur. Upon cooling from this temperature, ferrite is deposited first at the grain boundaries and then along certain crystallographic planes giving rise to a structure such as that shown in Fig. 5.3(*a*). This type of structure is often known as a Widmanstatten structure, since it was first observed by Widmanstatten in meteorites. The structure is associated with weakness and brittleness, but can be remedied by reannealing to the correct temperature.

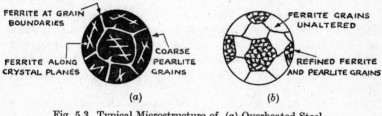

Fig. 5.3. Typical Microstructure of (*a*) Overheated Steel
(*b*) Under-annealed Steel

Burning

If a steel is heated far above the upper critical range to temperatures approaching the solidus, fusion and subsequent oxidation occur at the grain boundaries. Brittle films of oxide are formed which make the steel unsuitable for further use. The steel is said to be 'burnt' and must be remelted.

Under-annealing

Under-annealed structures are more frequently observed in the heat-affected zones of the parent metal in the welding of mild steel. The steel is heated to within the critical range, that is, between the upper and lower critical points. At this temperature the original pearlite will have changed to several small austenite grains. Upon cooling, ferrite is deposited at the austenite grain boundaries, the residual austenite transforming to pearlite at the eutectoid temperature. The resulting structure is similar to that shown in Fig. 5.3(*b*).

(c) Spheroidizing Annealing

High-carbon steels may be softened by annealing at 650°–700°C. (just below the lower critical range, Fig. 5.1), when the cementite of the pearlite balls up or spheroidizes. The resulting structure is one of cementite globules in a ferrite matrix. In this condition the steels can be cold drawn and possess good machinability. Spheroidization is more readily carried out on a fine pearlite structure when fine globules of cementite are obtained. Large globules, although producing a softer structure, present difficulties in machining and produce a poor surface.

2. NORMALIZING

For hypo-eutectoid steels, normalizing consists of heating the steel to 30°–50°C. above the upper critical range, holding it at this temperature for a time depending upon the section thickness, followed by AIR cooling.

Normalizing produces maximum grain refinement, and consequently the steel is slightly harder and stronger than a fully annealed steel. However, the properties obtained in normalizing will vary with section thickness. Large sections, which cool very slowly, may exhibit properties very similar to those of a fully annealed steel.

It will be noted from Fig. 5.1 that the normalizing temperatures for hyper-eutectoid steels are above the upper critical range since a sufficiently fast air cooling prevents grain boundary precipitation of the cementite.

3. HARDENING

Hardening of hypo-eutectoid steels involves heating to 30°–50°C. above the upper critical range, holding the steel at this temperature for a time depending upon the thickness, followed by quenching in water, brine or oil.

The effect of cooling rate on the transformation temperature and products of austenite is shown in Fig. 5.4.

With very slow cooling the austenite transforms to lamellar pearlite. Increasing the cooling rate depresses the transformation temperature, giving a finer, harder pearlite, until a second transformation occurs at 150° to 350°C. when martensite is formed. When a certain cooling rate, known as the *critical cooling rate*, has been exceeded, the austenite transforms direct to martensite. Martensite is the hardest structure in a given steel, and therefore to harden a steel fully the critical cooling rate must be exceeded.

The critical cooling rate is lowered with increasing carbon and alloy content. With certain alloy steels full hardening may be obtained by oil quenching (oil-hardening steels) or even air cooling (air-hardening steels).

There is no sharp line of demarcation between the structures obtained with various cooling rates, but the following terms are used.

LAMELLAR PEARLITE (Fig. 5.4)

A coarsely laminated structure, consisting of alternate laminations of ferrite and cementite, obtained upon very slow cooling.

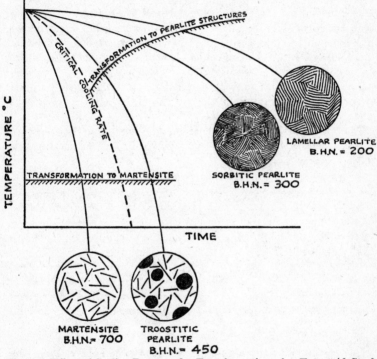

Fig. 5.4. Effect of Cooling Rate on the Transformation of a Eutectoid Steel

SORBITIC PEARLITE (Fig. 5.4)

A finely laminated structure obtained by a faster rate of cooling. The laminations are closer together and may only be resolved with difficulty, if at all, at normal magnifications. Hardness and strength increase as the fineness of the pearlite increases.

TROOSTITIC PEARLITE (Fig. 5.4)

This consists of dark-etching nodules of pearlite, obtained by a more rapid rate cooling such as oil quenching. At high magnifications the

41

dark nodules are found to consist of laminations radiating from a central nucleus. The nodules are usually associated with some martensite. This structure may be known as *Primary Troostite* to distinguish it from the troostite obtained upon tempering, which we shall call *Secondary Troostite*.

MARTENSITE (Fig. 5.4)

This is the hardest structure in a given steel, the hardness depending upon the carbon content. It is seen as a hard needle-like structure under the microscope. Martensite is a super-saturated solid solution of carbon in α iron. When austenite is quenched to room temperature the carbon atoms become 'locked' in the α iron lattice, causing lattice distortion and subsequent hardening. Softening only occurs by reheating or tempering the martensite when the carbon is precipitated.

The effect of carbon content on the maximum hardness of quenched steels, together with average hardening temperatures, is given in Table 5.1.

Carbon %	0·2	0·3	0·4	0·5	0·6	0·7	0·8–1·4
Average Hardening Temperature °C.	870	850	830	810	790	770	760
V.P.N.	490	590	690	770	820	840	860

Table 5.1. Effect of Carbon Content on Maximum Hardness of Quenched Steels together with Average Hardening Temperatures

In practice full hardening may not always be achieved and the range of hardness values obtained is shown in Fig. 5.5.

HARDENABILITY. 'MASS EFFECT'

The terms hardness and hardenability should not be confused. Hardenability can be defined as the ability of a steel to be hardened by quenching, and is related to the depth and distribution of hardness throughout a section. It is not related to maximum hardness, which depends almost entirely on carbon content (Fig. 5.5), and not to any extent on alloy content, e.g. a water-quenched 0·9% carbon steel will possess a higher maximum hardness than a 3% nickel steel containing only 0·3% carbon. However, the latter will possess the greater hardenability since it will harden fully throughout a larger section.

For full hardening the actual cooling rate throughout the section must exceed the critical cooling rate for that steel. Actual cooling rate depends upon (*a*) the quenching medium, and (*b*) the diameter

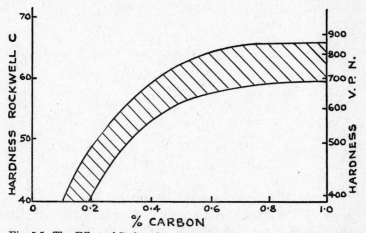

Fig. 5.5. The Effect of Carbon Content on the Hardness of Quenched Steel in Practice

of the bar or thickness of section. Plain carbon steels possess a high critical cooling rate and therefore large sections cannot be fully hardened throughout (Fig. 5.6).

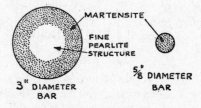

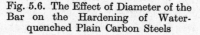

Fig. 5.6. The Effect of Diameter of the Bar on the Hardening of Water-quenched Plain Carbon Steels

It is obvious from Fig. 5.6 that the mechanical properties obtained by heat-treating a 3-in.-diameter bar will be different from those obtained in a ⅝-in.-diameter bar of the same steel. In view of this, the term 'ruling section' has been introduced. If the 'ruling section' is exceeded, the stated mechanical properties will no longer apply, since hardening of the core will be incomplete. The critical cooling rate is reduced by the addition of alloying elements, and alloy steels are therefore not so liable to 'mass-effect' (Fig. 5.7).

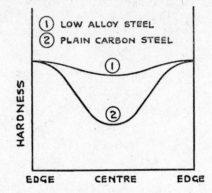

Fig. 5.7. Cross-section Hardenability of two Steels

4. TEMPERING

Tempering of hardened steel involves reheating to just below the lower critical range. The rate of cooling after tempering is not important for plain carbon steels. The objects of tempering are:

1. To relieve internal stresses induced by quenching.
2. To toughen the steel.

Tempering at 100°–200°C. is sufficient to relieve quenching stresses. When the temperature is in the region 200°–450°C. the martensite decomposes into ferrite and the precipitation of fine particles of carbide occurs. The fine granular structure formed is known as *secondary troostite* and must not be confused with the *primary troostite* of quenching which is laminated. This results in some toughening at the expense of hardness.

At higher temperatures 450°–650°C. the carbide particles coalesce into larger particles, thereby decreasing the strength and hardness while further increasing the toughness. The granular structure of carbide particles in a ferrite matrix is known as *sorbite* (Fig. 5.8). This structure is associated with maximum toughness.

Fig. 5.8. Sorbite

Sorbite is the ideal microstructure for heat-treated components subject to dynamic stresses, e.g. axles, crankshafts and connecting rods.

It should be noted that there is no strict line of demarcation between *secondary troostite* and *sorbite*; the distinction is a matter of size of the precipitated carbide particles.

The effect of tempering on the hardness of a quenched eutectoid steel is shown in Fig. 5.9.

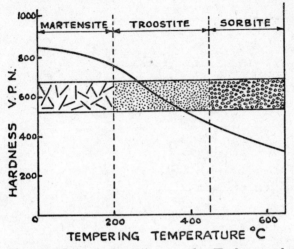

Fig. 5.9. Effect of Tempering on the Hardness and Microstructure of a Quenched Eutectoid Steel

THE ISOTHERMAL TRANSFORMATION OF AUSTENITE

The behaviour of steels, when cooled at different rates from the austenitic state, may be understood more fully by studying the constant temperature or isothermal transformations of austenite. These transformations may be studied by heating several small specimens of the steel to above the upper critical range, followed by quenching rapidly into a constant temperature bath of molten lead or molten salt. The specimens are withdrawn at definite intervals and quenched in water (Fig. 5.10). This treatment converts any untransformed austenite to martensite and the amount of martensite is estimated by microscopic examination. In this way the extent of transformation at this temperature can be studied at various time intervals.

If the times for the beginning and end of transformation are plotted for each temperature, a curve is obtained (Fig. 5.11) known as the S curve, or T.T.T. (Time-Temperature-Transformation) curve for that steel.

At higher temperatures the austenite will transform to pearlite, ranging from lamellar to troostitic pearlite as the temperature of

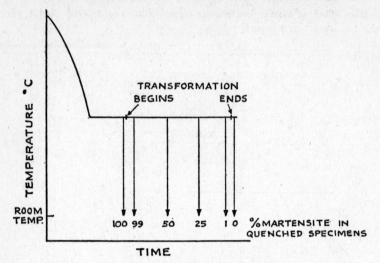

Fig. 5.10. Technique of Studying Isothermal Transformations

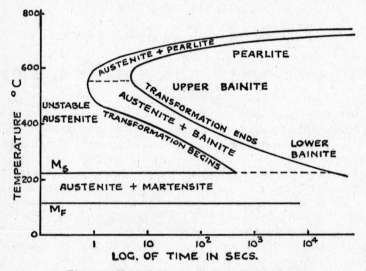

Fig. 5.11. Typical S-curve for Plain Carbon Steel

transformation decreases. At intermediate temperatures a black rapid etching structure known as bainite is obtained, which at higher temperatures is feathery (*upper bainite*) and at lower temperatures needle-like (*lower bainite*). Lower bainite is not easy to distinguish from martensite, but is not as hard as the latter. The Ms and

Mf temperatures denote the temperatures for the beginning and end of the transformation to martensite. These temperatures will depend upon the composition of the steel. Below the Ms temperature the austenite will transform to white slow etching martensite.

HEAT-TREATMENTS BASED ON THE 'S' CURVE

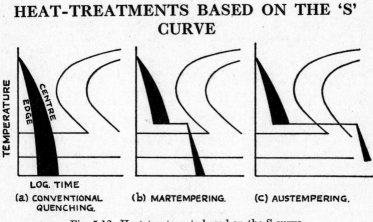

(a) CONVENTIONAL QUENCHING.　　(b) MARTEMPERING.　　(C) AUSTEMPERING.

Fig. 5.12. Heat-treatments based on the S-curve
Cooling Curves shown for Edge and Centre of Steel being treated

The change from austenite (γ iron) to martensite (α iron) is accompanied by volume change and since the cooling rate will vary across the section thickness, distortion and quenching cracks are likely to occur upon direct hardening (Fig. 5.12(a)). The processes of austempering and martempering are an attempt to avoid the distortion which is usually associated with the martensite reaction.

MARTEMPERING

The steel is heated to above the upper critical range and quenched into a salt bath maintained at a temperature just above the Ms temperature (Fig. 5.12(b)). It is held in the bath until the temperature is uniform throughout the section, when it is cooled in air. Martensite is thus formed with a minimum of distortion and danger of cracking. The time required for equalization of temperature throughout the section should not exceed that for the beginning of the transformation to bainite. It is therefore limited to relatively small-section work, particularly of complicated design.

AUSTEMPERING

The steel is heated to above the upper critical range and quenched into a molten salt or lead bath, maintained at a temperature in the bainitic region (250°–500°C.). It is held in the bath until the austenite has transformed to bainite, when it is cooled to room temperature at any desired rate (Fig. 5.12(c)).

The tensile and impact properties of austempered low- and medium-carbon steels are generally inferior to those of fully hardened and tempered steels. However, austempering is an advantage when dealing with work of complicated section, which might distort or crack when quenched in the conventional manner.

PRACTICAL ASPECTS OF HEAT-TREATMENT

FURNACE ATMOSPHERES

The control of furnace atmosphere is particularly important in the heat-treatment of steel in order to avoid such defects as oxidation or scaling, decarburization (resulting in a soft skin) or carburization (resulting in a hard skin).

In gas- and oil-fired furnaces, where the products of combustion come into contact with the steel being heated, it is essential to control the extent of the combustion of the fuel. Depending upon the volume of air used to burn the fuel, furnace atmospheres may be divided into three main types, namely oxidizing, reducing, or neutral. An oxidizing atmosphere contains an excess of oxygen and may give rise to scaling and decarburization of the surface of the steel. A reducing atmosphere contains an excess of carbon monoxide, due to insufficient air being used for combustion. Although scaling is avoided, this may result in carburization of the surface. A neutral atmosphere contains no free oxygen and little, if any, carbon monoxide. Such an atmosphere, which is not harmful, is the result of complete combustion, which is difficult to achieve in practice.

In gas-fired muffle furnaces (Fig. 5.13) the products of combustion do not make contact with the steel being treated. In these

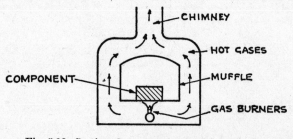

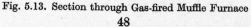

Fig. 5.13. Section through Gas-fired Muffle Furnace

furnaces, as in electric furnaces, the steel is in contact with an air atmosphere. Scaling and decarburization will therefore take place, particularly at the higher temperatures. In such cases, artificial atmospheres may be used in heat-treatment furnaces. The air is purged out of the furnace and replaced by a controlled artificial atmosphere, at just above atmospheric pressure to prevent air entering the furnace. Various controlled atmospheres are in use, such as partially burnt town gas or partially burnt anhydrous 'cracked' ammonia.

LIQUID BATHS

Freedom from scaling and uniformity of heating can be obtained by immersing the steel in molten salt or molten metal baths. Various salt analyses are available for use at the temperatures involved in all heat-treatment operations. Neutral salts are used for such heating operations, but for liquid cyaniding (Chapter 6) carburizing salts are employed.

QUENCHING MEDIA

The chief quenching media, in order of their cooling rates, are brine solutions, water, oil and air. Water quenching is essential for the full hardening of plain carbon steels. However, upon quenching, an insulating blanket of steam tends to form between the metal and the water, thus appreciably reducing the cooling rate. The steel should therefore be agitated in the bath after quenching. As the temperature of the water in the quenching tank rises, the quench is less effective, since the tendency to form steam around the component increases. Brine solutions (e.g. sodium chloride in water) give a more drastic quench for two reasons. First, the solution has a higher boiling point, and secondly, the salt is effective in removing the scale, thus facilitating contact between clean steel and the quenching medium. However, such drastic quenching is not always necessary and may result in distortion or cracking. Alloy steels, which have a lower critical cooling rate, may be effectively hardened by oil quenching or even air cooling.

QUENCHING CRACKS AND DISTORTION

In addition to the normal thermal contraction, certain volume changes occur rapidly and unevenly throughout the section, when steel is quenched from the austenitic region. The change from austenite (face-centred cubic lattice) to martensite (body-centred cubic lattice) is accompanied by an expansion. This change occurs first at the outside of the section, which cools more quickly than the centre. In the centre of a large section, a contraction may occur where a troostitic pearlite structure has formed. Internal stresses are set up, which are likely to give rise to distortion or even cracking. The cracking may occur some time after quenching and occasionally during tempering.

QUENCHING TECHNIQUE

Distortion can be minimized by bearing in mind a few simple points. For example, cylindrical specimens should be quenched vertically, flat sections edgeways, and the thicker section of a non-uniform component should enter the quenching bath first.

THE RELATIONSHIP OF DESIGN TO HEAT-TREATMENT

Distortion and cracking in heat-treatment can frequently be traced to bad design of the component. Steel articles which have to be heat-treated should be designed so that the cooling rate is as uniform as possible throughout the section. This can be achieved by avoiding large variations in cross-section. Sharp changes in section should be avoided by providing generous fillets. Fig. 5.14(a) shows a badly designed punch. In the improved design (Fig. 5.14(b)) the thickness of

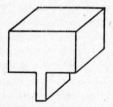
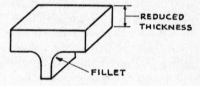

(a) Incorrect design   (b) Improved design

Fig. 5.14. The Effect of Design in Heat-treatment

the horizontal portion has been reduced and a fillet provided, so as to give a more uniform cooling rate. In some cases holes may be drilled in the heaviest sections to reduce the mass without any adverse effect on the application of the article.

6. The Surface Hardening of Steel

It is frequently necessary for machine parts to possess a hard, wear-resisting surface and yet be sufficiently tough to withstand dynamic stresses. These properties are obtained by treating a tough steel, so as to increase the hardness of its surface. There are four important processes of surface hardening, namely:

1. Case hardening
2. Nitriding
3. Flame hardening
4. Induction hardening

Processes (1) and (2) involve a change in chemical composition of surface, whereas (3) and (4) involve only a change in microstructure by local heat-treatment.

CASE HARDENING

In case hardening, a low-carbon steel is heated to above the upper critical range, in a carbon-rich material. In this way the carbon content of the surface is increased to about 0·85% carbon. When followed by heat-treatment, a hard wear-resisting surface is obtained. The carbon-rich material may be solid, liquid or gaseous.

(a) Solid carburizing (pack carburizing)
The steel components (finish-machined or a little oversize) are packed in a solid carburizing mixture in steel boxes, whose lids are sealed with clay, to exclude air. The box is heated at 900°–950°C. for three to eight hours, depending upon the depth of case required. After carburizing, the components are allowed to cool slowly in the box. The solid carburizing mixture may consist of charcoal or powdered coke, together with an energizer, such as barium carbonate. Various proprietary compounds are available on the market for

this purpose. Any portion of the surface which is not required to be carburized may be copper-plated to a thickness of 0·003 in.

The exact mechanism of carburization is not fully understood, but the barium carbonate provides oxygen to oxidize part of the carbon to carbon monoxide. The carbon monoxide dissociates at the surface of the work, according to the chemical equation $2\ CO \rightarrow CO_2 + C$, and the freshly produced or 'nascent' carbon is absorbed by the steel. The rate of diffusion of the carbon into the steel will depend upon the carburizing temperature, and the composition of the steel and of the carburizing mixture.

In general, case depths of between 0·025 in.–0·060 in. are usually obtained by this method. When carburizing at 900°C., about one hour at temperature should be allowed for each 0·010 in. of case depth.

(b) Liquid carburizing

The steel components, contained in a wire basket, are immersed in a bath of molten salt, maintained at a temperature of 870°–950°C. The parts are usually quenched upon withdrawal. The salt mixture usually contains sodium cyanide (20–45%) together with sodium carbonate and sodium chloride.

Heating is rapid and uniform, and distortion is minimized. The process is economical for thin cases on small parts, and is used mainly for cases of up to 0·010 in. on mild-steel components subjected to light loads. Such case depths can be obtained in about forty-five minutes. The maximum economical case depth is about 0·030 in., which may be obtained in about three hours.

A certain amount of nitriding also occurs, in addition to carburizing. The presence of sodium chloride 'activates' the cyanide, giving rise to an increase in carburizing action and a decrease in the nitriding action.

It is important to emphasize the dangers involved in the use of cyanide for hardening. Salt baths should be fitted with a hood to remove all fumes. Care should be taken to avoid burns due to splashing, and to prevent cyanide from entering the blood stream via cuts or sores.

(c) Gas carburizing

Carburizing can be conveniently carried out by heating the component to approximately 900°C. in a suitable gaseous atmosphere. The gases usually employed include treated town gas, ethane, propane and butane. The case depths vary from 0·01–0·04 in. and carburizing times are usually up to four hours.

HEAT-TREATMENT OF CARBURIZED STEEL

If the carbon content of the case, after carburizing, is more than approximately 0·85% carbon, some free cementite may be deposited at the grain boundaries, on cooling slowly from the carburizing temperature. This would result in embrittlement and the risk of 'flaking' or 'peeling' of the case in service. Since carburizing involves prolonged heating at a high temperature, grain growth will occur in both the core and the case, and heat-treatment is necessary in order to obtain optimum properties. The carbon content of the case (0·85%) is different from that of the core (0·2% carbon), consequently a double heat-treatment is required (Fig. 6.1).

1. *CORE REFINING*

The steel is first heated to just above the upper critical range for the core (approx. 870°C.), when the core consists of fine-grained austenite. After soaking at this temperature it is then quenched in water or oil, to produce a core structure consisting of small particles of ferrite, embedded in martensite.

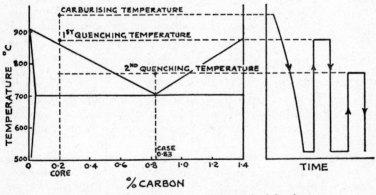

Fig. 6.1. Heat-treatment of Carburized Steel

However, 870°C. is well above the usual quenching temperature for a steel containing 0·85% carbon and consequently, after this treatment, the case will consist of a coarse martensite which is hard and brittle. A further treatment is therefore necessary to refine the case.

2. *CASE REFINING*

The steel is heated to just above the critical range for the case

(760°C.) when the case consists of fine grains of austenite. Subsequent quenching from this temperature results in a fine-grained martensite which is hard, but not excessively brittle.

At 760°C. the core will consist of fine grains of austenite in a ferrite matrix. Upon quenching from this temperature, a structure of small martensite particles in a matrix of ferrite and troostitic pearlite is obtained. An improvement in core toughness can be obtained by rapid heating through the range 650°–760°C. followed by quenching without soaking. This treatment reduces the amount of martensite in the core.

A final tempering at 150°C. is advisable to relieve quenching stresses.

Case-hardening Steels

Mild steels and low alloy steels of the nickel or nickel-chromium type are chiefly employed for case-hardening.

CASE-HARDENING MILD STEELS

The carbon content may vary from 0·1% where maximum core toughness is required to 0·3% carbon, where higher load-carrying capacity is required. The manganese content should be approximately 0·6–0·9%. Manganese aids carburizing and increases the depth of hardening, but the amount should be controlled, since it increases the tendency to distortion and cracking during heat-treatment.

ALLOY CASE-HARDENING STEELS

These steels usually contain about 0·15% carbon and 2–5% nickel. Chromium may also be present such that the Ni:Cr ratio is approximately 3:1. The effect of nickel in case-hardening steels may be summarized as follows:

1. Nickel reduces the critical cooling rate so that oil quenching may be substituted for water quenching, with less risk of distortion and cracking.

2. Grain growth, during carburizing, is restrained and in consequence the core refining treatment may, in certain cases, be eliminated.

3. The tendency towards cracking during grinding and flaking of the case is considerably reduced.

4. Improved yield point and ultimate tensile strength is obtained without any reduction in toughness.

5. The rate of diffusion of carbon is slightly reduced, consequently the time required for a given case depth is increased.

The effect of chromium is to increase the wear resistance of the

54

case. Improvement in strength is also obtained without serious loss of toughness. 'Mass-effect' is considerably reduced by the use of low alloy nickel-chrome steels.

NITRIDING

A hard wear-resisting surface can be produced by using nitrogen instead of carbon, as the hardening agent. This process, known as nitriding, involves heating the finish-machined and heat-treated steel at 500°C. for 2–4 days in a gas-tight container, through which ammonia gas is circulated. The ammonia partially dissociates into nitrogen and hydrogen at the surface of the work, and the 'nascent' nitrogen diffuses into the surface, forming hard nitrides.

Plain carbon steels are not suitable for nitriding, since iron nitrides are formed which make the case too brittle. Special alloy steels are employed for nitriding, e.g. those of the *Nitralloy* type which contain 0·2–0·5% carbon, 1½% chromium, 1% aluminium and 0·2% molybdenum. Hard nitrides of chromium and aluminium are formed in the surface layers. Chromium nitride diffuses to a greater depth than aluminium nitride, consequently hardness falls off more gradually from the surface to the core. The presence of molybdenum gives grain refinement and improves the toughness of the core.

Heat-treatment is carried out prior to nitriding, in order to obtain a tough core. The full sequence of operations for a Nitralloy steel, similar to that mentioned, would be as follows:

1. Oil hardening from 900°C.
2. Tempering at 650°C.
3. Rough machining
4. Stabilizing anneal at 525°–550°C. for up to 5 hours to remove machining stresses
5. Finish machining
6. Nitriding at 500°C. to give a case hardness of 1,050–1,100 V.P.N. The usual case depth varies between 0·010 in. and 0·035 in.

Typical applications of nitriding are die blocks, link pins, spindles, brake-drums, moulds for plastics, crankshafts, and printing dies.

Improved core properties can be obtained by the use of aluminium free steels. This is achieved at the expense of surface hardness which is reduced to about 750–900 V.P.N. Examples of such steels are the 3% Cr-Mo and 3% Cr-Mo-V type, the latter containing 0·7–1·2% molybdenum and 0·1–0·3% vanadium.

Austenitic and ferritic heat-resisting and stainless steels can be successfully nitrided, following a special surface preparation. The

E

nitriding temperature is usually 550°C. High-speed tool steels may be nitrided after the conventional treatment to increase the surface hardness. Certain alloy cast irons containing aluminium and chromium may be nitrided to give a surface hardness of 900–950 V.P.N. The nitrided cast iron has a good corrosion and wear resistance and is used for cylinder linings and piston rings.

Compared with other processes of surface hardening, nitriding possesses a number of advantages, i.e.:

1. Distortion and quenching cracks are avoided since heat-treatment is carried out prior to nitriding. After nitriding, the parts are stress free.

2. A very hard surface (1,050–1,100 V.P.N.) can be obtained. The maximum hardness is usually obtained 0·001 in.–0·003 in. below the surface.

3. The hardness of the case is retained up to 500°C. in service. Carburized cases would begin to soften above 200°C.

4. The nitrided surface possesses a good resistance to corrosion, and for maximum corrosion resistance the parts should be used as they come from the nitriding container.

5. Nitrided steels have a good resistance to fatigue.

Nitriding would be a relatively expensive process for the surface hardening of small numbers of components, due to the initial high cost of plant and the necessity of using special alloy steels. However, the process is relatively cheap when large numbers of components are to be treated.

Carbonitriding is strictly a modification of the gas-carburizing process. It involves the simultaneous carburizing and nitriding of a plain carbon steel, by heating in a controlled atmosphere composed of ammonia and hydrocarbon gases. The temperature employed ranges from 650°–950°C., depending upon the steel and the depth of case required, but the usual temperature is about 820°–840°C. The steel may be quenched upon removal from the furnace. Subsequent heat-treatment is not necessary and there is less distortion, since a lower operating temperature is employed. The process is particularly applicable for hard, shallow, wear-resisting cases for automobile components.

FLAME HARDENING (THE SHORTER PROCESS)

The steel surface is heated to just above the upper critical range, by means of a moving oxy-acetylene torch, followed immediately by quenching, using a water spray attached to the torch.

The steels used should contain 0·4–0·6% carbon, in order to

ensure hardness of the surface whilst retaining reasonable toughness of the core. With 0·45% carbon, a surface hardness of 600–650 V.P.N. is obtained, whilst the depth of hardening is usually about 0·12 in.–0·15 in.

The process is applied to gears, spindles, cams, clutches, sprockets, pinions, and the worms for worm-reduction units.

Before hardening, the parts should be stress free, and a low-temperature stress-relief anneal is usual after hardening.

INDUCTION HARDENING (THE TOCCO PROCESS)

The surface to be hardened is surrounded by a perforated inductor block, through which a high-frequency current is passed. The surface is quickly heated by the induced eddy currents to just above the upper critical temperature in about 3–5 seconds. Quenching is then carried out by spraying with water through the holes in the inductor block. A case depth of approximately $\frac{1}{8}$ in. is obtained by this method, using similar steels to those used for flame hardening.

If the process is closely controlled, due to the speed of operation grain growth, decarburization and distortion are prevented.

7. Alloy Steels

The properties of plain carbon steels have already been discussed in Chapter 4 and it will be realized that such steels have many limitations:

1. It is not possible to obtain an ultimate tensile strength of greater than 45 tons per square inch, if reasonable toughness and ductility are also desired.

2. Plain carbon steels are liable to 'mass effect'. Large sections cannot therefore be effectively hardened.

3. Drastic water quenching is necessary for full hardening, with consequent risk of cracking and distortion.

4. Plain carbon steels have a poor resistance to corrosion and to oxidation at elevated temperatures.

In order to overcome these limitations and to meet the specific requirements of engineers, alloy steels have been developed. The principal alloying elements are nickel, chromium, manganese, molybdenum, silicon, tungsten, vanadium, cobalt and copper.

EFFECT OF ALLOYING ELEMENTS

The effect of an alloying element may be one or more of the following:

1. It may strengthen the steel by going into solid solution. The formation of a solid solution (Chapter 3) results in distortion of the crystal lattice structure, which increases the hardness and strength.

2. When the solid solubility limit has been exceeded, the alloying element may form hard carbides. These carbides are usually associated with the cementite. Examples of carbide-forming elements are manganese, chromium, tungsten, and vanadium. Complex carbides are present in high-speed tool steels.

3. Certain alloying elements may give rise to the formation of graphite, which considerably reduces the strength, ductility and shock-resistance of the steel. Silicon, nickel and aluminium are

graphitizing elements and it is usual to counteract their effect by adding carbide-forming elements also.

4. It may refine or coarsen the grain. Nickel tends to refine the grain, whilst silicon and chromium are grain-coarsening elements.

5. It may lower the carbon content of the eutectoid structure, pearlite. Certain low alloy steels may therefore possess more pearlite in their microstructure than that expected from the carbon content.

6. It may *raise* or *lower* the critical points, thereby stabilizing *ferrite* or *austenite* respectively.

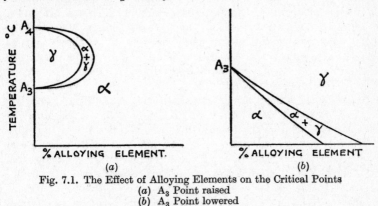

Fig. 7.1. The Effect of Alloying Elements on the Critical Points
(a) A_3 Point raised
(b) A_3 Point lowered

In Fig. 7.1(a) the A_3 point is raised until it merges with the A_4 point to form what is known as a 'closed gamma loop'. Thus, above a certain percentage of alloying element, ferrite (a iron) is stable at all temperatures. Such alloys are not heat-treatable, since they have no critical points. Grain refinement can only be carried out by annealing after cold-work. Elements which stabilize ferrite are chromium, silicon, tungsten, vanadium and molybdenum.

In Fig. 7.1(b) the A_3 point is lowered and after a certain percentage of alloying element, austenite (γ iron) is stable at room temperatures. Elements which stabilize austenite are nickel, manganese, cobalt and copper. Such steels are austenitic on air cooling to room temperature and cannot be hardened by the normal quenching technique.

7. It may lower the critical cooling rate of the steel, thus increasing its hardenability. Alloy steels can be fully hardened in larger sections than plain carbon steels. In addition, oil quenching can be substituted for the more drastic water quenching, thus minimizing the tendency to distortion and cracking. In certain alloy steels, the critical cooling rate may be reduced sufficiently to produce a martensitic structure on air cooling (air-hardening steels).

59

In addition to the general effects mentioned above, certain alloying elements may produce characteristic effects, e.g. the improvement in corrosion resistance by the addition of chromium. Tungsten and cobalt are noted for their effect on magnetic properties and vanadium for its effect in 'cleansing' a steel, making it free from inclusions.

CLASSIFICATION OF ALLOY STEELS

Alloy steels may be classified in many ways, but for the purposes of our study it is convenient to use a structural classification as follows:

1. *LOW ALLOY STEELS* which possess slowly cooled microstructures, similar to those of plain carbon steels in the same condition, namely pearlite, pearlite + ferrite or pearlite + cementite. These low alloy steels are often referred to as 'pearlitic' alloy steels.

2. *HIGH ALLOY STEELS* which possess slowly cooled microstructures, consisting either of martensite, austenite or ferrite + carbide particles. The reason for the presence of these structures has already been discussed.

In this chapter, an attempt will be made to study alloy steels from a structural standpoint. *The connection between the percentage of a single alloying element and the microstructure of the steel is affected by variations in cooling rate (size of section) and in the amount of other elements present, e.g. carbon. These limitations should be borne in mind in the following treatment of the subject.*

The effect of various alloying elements on the properties of steel will now be considered.

MANGANESE

Manganese goes into solid solution, increasing the strength and hardness, and also forms hard carbides. It lowers the critical cooling rate, thus increasing the hardenability of the steel and giving rise to air-hardening martensitic steels. Manganese lowers the critical range, thus stabilizing the austenite. Manganese steels may be conveniently classified as follows:

Approximate Manganese %	Type of Structure
0–2	Pearlitic
2–12	Martensitic
12–100	Austenitic

Table 7.1. Structural Classification of Manganese Steels

This classification is only approximate as previously stated, but provides a useful basis for study.

PEARLITIC MANGANESE STEELS

These steels have to some extent replaced the more expensive pearlitic nickel steels. They contain about 1·5% manganese and 0·3–0·4% carbon, with in some cases 0·2–0·55% molybdenum. The presence of molybdenum reduces 'mass effect' and for larger section work the molybdenum content should be at the higher end of this range. The full heat-treatment involves oil hardening from about 840°C. followed by tempering at 600–650°C. In this condition they are used for shafts, gears, spindles, connecting rods and swivel arms. The manganese-molybdenum steels have mechanical properties roughly equivalent to those of a $3\frac{1}{2}$% nickel steel.

MARTENSITIC MANGANESE STEEL

These air-hardening steels have no commercial importance.

AUSTENITIC MANGANESE STEEL

Hadfield's manganese steel, containing 12–14% manganese and 1% carbon, was one of the first alloy steels to be discovered and produced commercially. It was developed in 1882 by Sir Robert Hadfield at Sheffield.

The steel is heat-treated by water quenching from 1,000°C., when the carbides are taken into solid solution to give a uniform solid solution of austenite (Fig. 7.2). In this condition the alloy is soft, as measured by the normal indentation tests. The Brinell Hardness Number is about 200. However, the alloy has excellent wear-resisting properties, since abrasion converts the surface layers into a hard structure with a Brinell Hardness Number of about 550. The steel is used for rock drills, crushers, railway points and dredging equipment. The alloy is difficult to machine but may be forged or hot-rolled.

Fig. 7.2. Microstructure of Hadfield's Manganese Steel. Water-quenched 1,000°C. Twinned Crystals of Austenite

NICKEL

Nickel has a marked strengthening effect on the steel, since it goes into solid solution and decreases the carbon content of the eutectoid. It is a graphitizing element, but this effect may be counteracted by the presence of carbide-forming elements such as manganese or chromium. Nickel lowers the critical cooling rate, thereby increasing the hardenability of the steel. Oil- and air-hardening steels may be produced. It also lowers the critical range, thus stabilizing austenite. Nickel steels may be conveniently classified as follows, bearing in mind the limitations previously mentioned.

Approximate Nickel %	Structure
0–8	Pearlitic
8–22	Martensitic
22–100	Austenitic

Table 7.2. Structural Classification of Nickel Steels

PEARLITIC NICKEL STEELS

In practice such steels usually contain up to 5% nickel with 0·1–0·4% carbon. Those with a carbon content of 0·1–0·15% are suitable for case-hardening, whilst those containing 0·25–0·4% carbon are used in the heat-treated condition for parts subjected to dynamic stresses, e.g. crankshafts, axles and connecting rods.

The full heat-treatment usually involves oil hardening from 830°–860°C. followed by a tempering at 550°–650°C. to produce a tough steel. The minimum mechanical properties for typical nickel steels in the fully heat-treated condition are as follows:

B.S. 970	Type	Y.P.	U.T.S.	EL	Izod	B.H.N.	Ruling Section
En 21	3% Ni	36	50	20	40	223	2½″
		32	45	22	40	201	4″
En 22	3½% Ni	41	55	18	40	248	2½″
		36	50	20	40	223	4″

Table 7.3. Minimum Mechanical Properties of Typical Low Alloy Nickel Steels

MARTENSITIC NICKEL STEELS

These steels, like the martensitic manganese steels, are of no commercial importance.

AUSTENITIC NICKEL STEELS

The austenitic nickel steels are not commercially important but there are numerous austenitic iron-nickel alloys (carbon-free) which find wide application. These iron nickel alloys are used as low and controlled-expansion alloys and for their magnetic properties. Well-known industrial alloys of this type include *Invar*, *Kovar* and *Permalloy*.

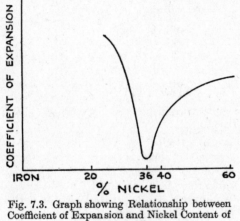

Fig. 7.3. Graph showing Relationship between Coefficient of Expansion and Nickel Content of Iron-nickel Alloys

Invar (36% Ni) has a very low coefficient of thermal expansion in the temperature range 0–100°C. (Fig. 7.3). It is used for watch and clock mechanisms, metal tapes, surveying instruments and thermostats.

Alloys with 30% nickel and up to 17% cobalt are used for making glass-to-metal seals in radio valves and other thermionic devices. These alloys have approximately the same coefficient of expansion as the harder glasses of the boro-silicate type and are known under such trade names as *Kovar*, *Nilo K*, and *Fernico*.

Permalloy (78·5% Ni) possesses a high magnetic permeability in weak magnetic fields (page 78).

CHROMIUM

Chromium goes into solid solution in the steel and also forms hard carbides. It lowers the carbon content of the eutectoid, and also the critical cooling rate, thereby increasing the hardenability of the steel. Chromium forms a 'closed gamma loop' and thus stabilizes

63

ferrite. It is a grain-coarsening element and therefore prolonged heating at high temperatures should be avoided. Chromium steels may be roughly classified as follows, bearing in mind the limitations previously mentioned.

Approx. Chromium%	Structure
0–2	Pearlitic
2–16	Martensitic
Above 16	Ferritic

Table 7.4. Structural Classification of Chromium Steels

PEARLITIC CHROMIUM STEELS

These steels usually contain 1·0–1·5% chromium and 0·35–1·0% carbon.

The medium-carbon steels may be oil hardened and tempered at 600°–650°C. to give a tough structure suitable for parts subjected to dynamic stresses, e.g. gears, axles, crankshafts and connecting rods. Steels containing 1·5% Cr and 0·2% V are used for springs. Chrome-vanadium spring steels are tempered at 420°C. and have an ultimate tensile strength of 90–100 tons per square inch.

The high-carbon steels are used for ball and roller bearings, small cold rolls, shoes for ore crushers and other components requiring a hard surface. These steels contain a higher proportion of free cementite than that indicated by the carbon content, and after heat-treatment this will be present in the spheroidized form. One important alloy in this group is En 31 containing 1·0% carbon and 1·4% chromium which is used for ball bearings. This steel is oil hardened from 810°C. and tempered at 150°C. to give a Brinell Hardness Number of 850.

MARTENSITIC CHROMIUM STEELS

Steels containing 1·0% carbon and 3·5% chromium are used in the oil-hardened condition for permanent magnets (page 76).

Complete resistance to atmospheric corrosion is obtained in steels with greater than about 12% chromium. This is due to the formation of a thin adherent oxide film on the surface which also provides resistance to corrosion by oxidizing solutions. These 'martensitic' stainless steels will be discussed more fully in the next chapter.

Chromium also increases the resistance to scaling at elevated temperatures and steels such as *Silchrome* (8% Cr 3·5% Si) are used for automobile valves.

FERRITIC CHROMIUM STEELS

These alloys containing 0·05–0·15% carbon and 16–30% chromium are usually known as the 'ferritic' stainless steels. They will be considered more fully in the following chapter.

NICKEL AND CHROMIUM

The alloying elements nickel and chromium are frequently used together and two main types of nickel chromium steel may be distinguished.

1. *LOW ALLOY NICKEL-CHROME STEELS*

These steels containing 1–5% nickel and 0·6–1·5% chromium are the most important alloys for general engineering purposes since a wide range of mechanical properties can be obtained by the appropriate heat-treatment.

2. *AUSTENITIC STAINLESS STEELS*

These are usually based on the 18:8 Cr:Ni type and will be discussed in the following chapter.

LOW ALLOY NICKEL-CHROME STEELS

The reason for the wide use of nickel-chrome steels is that the beneficial properties given by each element are additive, whereas the disadvantages associated with the use of either element singly are counteracted by the presence of the other element. For example the strength, ductility and toughness associated with nickel steel are combined with the hardness and wear resistance of chromium steels. The grain coarsening tendency of chromium is counteracted by the grain refining tendency of nickel, whilst the graphitizing tendency of nickel is counteracted by the carbide-forming tendency of chromium. These desirable properties are obtained by maintaining a Ni:Cr ratio of approximately 3:1.

The lower carbon steels (C=0·10–0·15%) are suitable for case hardening, whilst those with 0·25–0·35% carbon are used in the heat-treated condition for parts subjected to dynamic stresses, e.g. crankshafts, axles, connecting rods, swivel arms, etc. The full heat-treatment involves oil hardening from 820°–850°C. followed by tempering at 550°–650°C.

Nickel chrome steels are prone to a defect known as 'temper-brittleness'. This term usually refers to the drop in the Izod impact test value obtained by tempering in the range 250°–400°C., or by slow cooling through this range after tempering at 600°C. Such steels are not generally tempered in the range 250°–400°C. Temper-brittleness can be minimized by:

1. Oil quenching after tempering at 600°–650°C., or

2. The addition of 0·3–0·5% molybdenum to the steel. It is advisable to oil quench after tempering even if a Ni-Cr-Mo steel is used.

There is no complete explanation of temper-brittleness, which is only revealed by the Izod impact test.

Details of the minimum mechanical properties of typical nickel chrome steels in the fully heat-treated condition are given in Table 7.5.

B.S.970	Type	Y.P.	U.T.S.	EL	Izod	B.H.N.	Ruling Section Inches
En 23	3% Ni-Cr	52 38	65 50	16 20	35 40	293 223	2½ 6
En 27	3% Ni-Cr.-Mo	58 44	70 55	15 18	30 40	311 248	4 6
En 28	3½% Ni-Cr-Mo	68 48	80 60	14 17	25 35	263 269	2½ 6
En 30B	4¼% Ni-Cr-Mo	85	100	10	15	446	6

Table 7.5. The Minimum Mechanical Properties of Typical Nickel-chrome Steels in the Fully Heat-treated Condition

The 4¼% Ni-Cr-Mo steel is of the air-hardening type and is used for large-section work requiring freedom from distortion.

SILICON

Silicon lowers the carbon content of the eutectoid and forms a 'closed gamma loop'. It is a marked graphitizing element and steels with more than 5% silicon are commercially useless due to the presence of graphite. It has only a small effect on the hardenability since the graphitizing tendency exceeds the air-hardening tendency.

There are three important types of silicon steel, namely:

(1) *SILICO-MANGANESE STEEL.* Silicon $= 1.5-2.0\%$ Mn $= 0.6-1.0\%$
  Used for manufacture of leaf springs.
(2) *SILICON-STEEL* C $= 0.07\%$ Si $= 4\%$
  Possesses high magnetic permeability and electrical resistance and is used for transformer cores and the poles of dynamos and motors (page 77).
(3) *VALVE STEELS*
  Silicon is a secondary alloying element in automobile valve steels such as *SILCHROME* and *VALMAX* which contain 8% chromium and 3.5% silicon (page 73).

TUNGSTEN

Tungsten is a strong carbide-forming element. These carbides do not readily go into solid solution even at high temperatures. Hardened tungsten steels resist tempering up to relatively high temperatures, hence the use of tungsten in high-speed tool steels. Tungsten refines the grain size and decreases the tendency to decarburization during working. Tungsten increases coercive force and a steel containing 1% carbon and 6% tungsten is used for permanent magnets. Small amounts of tungsten are also present in certain heat- and corrosion-resisting steels.

MOLYBDENUM

Molybdenum is a strong carbide-forming element. It reduces 'mass-effect' and 'temper-brittleness' and inhibits grain growth. It is rarely used alone as an alloying element. Molybdenum improves the mechanical properties at high temperatures and 0.5% molybdenum is present in creep-resisting steels for use at high steam temperatures. It is used in high-speed tool steels, and heat- and corrosion-resisting steels.

VANADIUM

Vanadium is also a strong carbide-forming element and is used in high-speed tool steels. It is a grain-refining element and a strong deoxidizer. It ensures a clean steel by acting as a 'scavenger' for oxides and other inclusions.

8. Special Purpose Steels

Alloy steels have been developed to meet many requirements and in this chapter we shall consider some of the more important types of special alloy steels.

STAINLESS STEELS

Stainless steels were first discovered by Brearley in 1913 when he observed that a steel containing 13% chromium exhibited a good resistance to atmospheric corrosion. The corrosion resistance is due to the formation of a thin stable protective oxide film on the surface of the steel. This film also provides resistance against corrosive attack by solutions of an oxidizing nature.

The 13% chromium steel was the basis of the original stainless steel cutlery, but since that time many varieties of stainless steel have been developed. Stainless steels may be classified into three main types:

1. MARTENSITIC
2. AUSTENITIC
3. FERRITIC

MARTENSITIC STAINLESS STEELS

The martensitic stainless steels can be subdivided into three main types.

(a) *STAINLESS IRONS*
$$C = 0.07 - 0.10\%$$
$$Cr = 13\%$$

These alloys are usually air cooled or oil quenched from 950°–1,000° C. followed by tempering at 650°–750°C. In the hardened and tempered condition the alloy can be cold-worked and readily machined. It is readily welded and is used for turbine blades, split pins and rivets. The lower carbon alloys are used for domestic articles such as forks and spoons.

Typical mechanical properties for stainless iron in the hardened and tempered condition are:

Y.P.	U.T.S.	EL	B.H.N.
15–25	30–40	30–40	140–180

(b) *STAINLESS STEELS*

$$C = 0.2-0.4\%$$
$$Cr = 13\%$$

Hardening is carried out by oil quenching from 950°C. In this condition the steel possesses maximum corrosion resistance since all the carbides are in solid solution. Tempering at 500°–750°C. toughens the steel but lowers the corrosion resistance due to the precipitation of chromium-rich carbides. These alloys are difficult to weld and their corrosion resistance is decreased by cold-working. A high polish is necessary for maximum corrosion resistance.

The applications of these steels depend upon the carbon content.

0·2% carbon—used for valves and piston rods but should not be used in contact with copper-base alloys or graphitic packings owing to electrolytic action resulting in corrosion.

0·3% carbon—used for table cutlery, surgical and other instruments requiring a sharp cutting edge. The steel is usually tempered in the range 150°–180°C. for these applications.

0·4%–1·0% carbon—used for springs and ball bearings which work in a corrosive environment.

(c) *HIGH CHROMIUM—LOW NICKEL STAINLESS STEELS* e.g. S.80 containing 0·1% carbon, 18% chromium, 2% nickel. This steel combines good corrosion resistance with good mechanical properties obtained by heat-treatment. The heat-treatment involves oil hardening from 950°C. followed by tempering at 650°C. and in this condition typical mechanical properties are:

YP	U.T.S.	EL	B.H.N.
40–50	55–65	15–25	250–320

It may be used in contact with graphite packings and copper-base alloys and typical applications include pump rods and shafts, regulator valves, blow-off cocks, turbine blading and aircraft fittings.

AUSTENITIC STAINLESS STEELS

There are numerous austenitic stainless steels but most are based on the 18:8 Cr:Ni type. These alloys cannot be hardened by quench-

Fig. 8.1. Micro-structure of 18:8 Cr:Ni Stainless Steel, Water-quenched 1,050°C. Twin-ned Crystals of Austenite

ing. Quenching from 1,050°C. results in the carbides being taken into solid solution to give a fully austenitic structure (Fig. 8.1). In this state the alloy is soft and non-magnetic, and exhibits maximum corrosion resistance. Typical mechanical properties for a steel containing 0·1% carbon, 18% chromium and 8% nickel after water quenching are:

YP	U.T.S.	EL	R.A.	B.H.N.
16–20	40–50	40–60	40–60	160–200

The chief uses are for chemical plant construction and for domestic and decorative purposes.

If austenitic stainless steels are heated in the temperature range 500°–800°C. precipitation of chromium-rich carbides occurs at the grain boundaries resulting in a decrease in the corrosion resistance. This is due partly to the resulting chromium deficiency in the grains and partly to the electrolytic action between the carbide particles and the matrix.

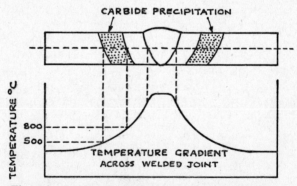

Fig. 8.2. Carbide Precipitation in the Heat-affected Zones of the Plate in the Welding of 18:8 Stainless Steel

During welding the heat-affected zones of the plate are main-tained in this temperature range for sufficient time to allow carbide precipitation to occur. The phenomenon is therefore usually referred to as 'weld-decay'.

'Weld-decay' may be minimized or prevented by:

1. Water quenching from 1,050°C. after welding. This treatment takes the carbides back into solid solution but is not always practicable, particularly for large welded vessels.

2. Reducing the carbon content. This reduces the amount of carbide precipitated at the grain boundaries. 'Extra low carbon' stainless steels are now available with a maximum of 0·03% carbon.

3. The addition of 'stabilizing' elements such as titanium and niobium. These elements have a stronger affinity for carbon than that possessed by chromium. The precipitated carbides will therefore consist chiefly of titanium carbide or niobium carbide and consequently chromium impoverishment of the grains does not occur. Such steels are known as 'stabilized' stainless steels and should always be specified for welded construction. The amount of stabilizing element is given by the following formulae:

$$\% \text{ titanium } = 6 \times (\% \text{ carbon in excess of } 0·02\%)$$
$$\% \text{ niobium } = 10 \times (\% \text{ carbon in excess of } 0·02\%)$$

4. The addition of ferrite-forming elements, e.g. silicon, molybdenum, tungsten. These form ferrite 'islands' in the microstructure in which the carbide is precipitated when the steel is heated in the range 500°–800°C. In this way the formation of a continuous brittle film is avoided.

Steels of the 18:8 type may also contain molybdenum (3%) and copper (2%) to give resistance to corrosion by various solutions. When molybdenum is added for this purpose the nickel content may be raised to 10% in order to counteract the tendency to form ferrite. Machinability may be increased by the addition of 0·2% selenium. An austenitic stainless steel for deep drawing purposes contains approximately 12% each of nickel and chromium.

Development of Sigma Phase

Steels of the 18:8 type which, due to various additions, have an austenite-ferrite structure are often referred to as duplex steels. If a duplex steel is heated in the range 500°–900°C. for some time a brittle constituent known as SIGMA PHASE is formed from the ferrite. When duplex steels are required for use at elevated temperatures the amount of ferrite should therefore be kept at a minimum.

FERRITIC STAINLESS STEELS

The ferritic steels containing 0·05–0·15% carbon and 16–30%

F

chromium are not amenable to heat-treatment. The structure can only be refined by recrystallization after cold-working. The microstructure consists of ferrite grains and carbide particles. These steels are used for parts where mechanical properties are secondary to corrosion resistance and good workability.

HEAT-RESISTING STEELS

Heat-resisting steels are required for a wide variety of applications such as superheater tubes and pipes in steam power plant, aero-engine and automobile valves, furnace conveyors, retorts, oil cracking units, gas turbines, and glass-making machinery. Heat-resisting steels should possess the following properties:

(1) *Good creep resistance*
Creep is the slow plastic deformation which occurs under prolonged loading to elevated temperatures.

(2) *Resistance to oxidation and scaling*
The presence of chromium, silicon and aluminium produces hard adherent films on the surface which protect the alloy against further attack. The alloy should also be resistant to chemical attack by vapours and gases which might exist in service.

(3) *Structural stability*
From the dimensional standpoint it is essential that components for use at high temperatures should have a stable structure. Carbide precipitation at the grain boundaries and the formation of sigma phase should be avoided. Spheroidization of carbides leads to a marked reduction in creep resistance. Since absolute dimensional accuracy is not possible some allowances have to be made in design.

(4) *Specific properties*
Properties relating to a particular application must also be considered, e.g. machinability, weldability, fatigue properties, and coefficient of thermal expansion.

In order to meet these requirements a number of heat-resisting steels have been developed. These steels may be classified as follows:

1. LOW ALLOY STEELS (0·5% MOLYBDENUM)
2. CHROMIUM-SILICON VALVE STEELS
3. PLAIN CHROMIUM STEELS (12–30% CHROMIUM)
4. AUSTENITIC CHROMIUM-NICKEL STEELS

1. LOW ALLOY STEELS

The main applications for these steels are for superheater tubes and pipes in steam-power plants where service temperatures are in the range 400°–550°C. Typical compositions of suitable steels are those containing 0·5% Mo, 0·5% Mo + 1% Cr, 0·5% Mo + 0·25% V, 0·5% Mo + 2·25% Cr. These additions are all carbide-forming elements and such alloys undergo precipitation hardening when tempered in the range 600°–700°C. after normalizing.

2. VALVE STEELS

Chromium-silicon steels such as *Silchrome* (0·4 C 8 Cr 3·5 Si) and *Valmax* (0·5 C 8 Cr 3·5 Si 0·5 Mo) are used for automobile valves. They possess a good resistance to scaling at a dull red heat although their strength at elevated temperatures is relatively low. The use of motor fuel treated with tetraethyl lead has led to the development of *Silchrome XB* steel (En 59) with a better corrosion resistance. This is a Cr:Si:Ni steel containing approximately 20% Cr, 2% Si, 1·5% Ni. For aero-engines and marine diesel engines the 13/13/3 nickel-chromium-tungsten valve steel (En 54) is usually employed.

3. PLAIN CHROMIUM STEELS

These include the martensitic chromium steels (12–13% Cr) and the ferritic chromium steels (18–30% Cr).

Plain chromium steels are noted more for oxidation resistance at high temperatures than for their strength which is not high under such conditions. The maximum operating temperature for the martensitic steels is about 750°C., whereas for the ferritic steels it is about 1,000°–1,150°C. Such steels have a good resistance to sulphurous atmospheres.

4. AUSTENITIC CHROMIUM-NICKEL STEELS

The austenitic steels combine good mechanical properties at high temperatures with good scaling resistance. These alloys contain a minimum of 18% Cr and 8% Ni stabilized with titanium or niobium. Other carbide-forming elements such as molybdenum and tungsten may also be added. Carbide-forming elements improve creep strength by giving rise to precipitation hardening alloys. Such alloys are suitable for use up to 1,100°C. Austenitic steels are suitable for gas turbine discs and blades.

HIGH-SPEED TOOL STEELS

Plain carbon tool steels are unsuitable for high-speed machining since the heat produced by frictional effects would temper the hard martensitic structure. To meet the needs of modern machining practice special alloy high-speed tool steels have been developed.

The best known high-speed tool steel is that containing 0·6% carbon, 18% tungsten, 4% chromium, and 1% vanadium, known as the '18:4:1' type. These elements form hard carbides which resist tempering, thus improving the hardness at red heat.

Steels of the 18:4:1 type may also contain 5–12% cobalt. Cobalt improves 'red-hardness' and gives rise to a greater degree of 'secondary hardening' (below). Cobalt high-speed steels are particularly suitable for cutting hard, sandy or scaley material such as sand castings, cast iron and heat-treated steels.

During the 1939–45 war supplies of tungsten from the Far East were not readily available and 'substitute' steels were developed in which molybdenum replaced part of the tungsten. A typical steel is that of the '4:6' type containing 4% molybdenum, 6% tungsten, 4% chromium and 1% vanadium.

HARDENING OF HIGH-SPEED TOOL STEELS

In order to dissolve most of the carbides prior to quenching, a very high temperature of the order 1,250°–1,320°C. is required. However, at this temperature grain growth, decarburization and incipient fusion may occur and it is necessary to adopt a special heat-treatment technique. This is usually carried out in a two-chamber gas-fired furnace, preferably using a controlled atmosphere. The steel is preheated in the upper chamber to about 850°C. After 'soaking' at this temperature it is transferred to the lower chamber which is maintained at 1,250°–1,320°C. depending upon the composition of the steel. The time in the lower chamber is usually 1–3 minutes for small tools. It is then usually oil quenched, when the microstructure will consist of particles of carbides in a matrix of martensite and retained austenite.

Secondary Hardening

The quenched steel can be further hardened by tempering at 550°–570°C. (Fig. 8.3). This phenomenon, known as 'secondary hardening', is thought to be due to the transformation of retained austenite to martensite. The higher the alloy content of the steel

74

the more it responds to secondary hardening. Tempering at lower temperatures 350°–400°C. would result in softening (Fig. 8.3).

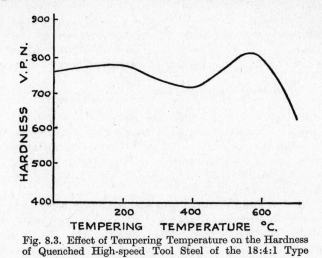

Fig. 8.3. Effect of Tempering Temperature on the Hardness of Quenched High-speed Tool Steel of the 18:4:1 Type

CEMENTED CARBIDE TOOLS

Cemented carbide tools are made by powder metallurgy and consist of hard tungsten carbide with or without the carbides of tantalum, vanadium, molybdenum and titanium, bonded with 6–20% cobalt. The ingredients in powdered form are pressed to shape and sintered at 1,500°C. when bonding occurs aided by partial melting of the cobalt. Well-known examples are *Widia* and *Cutanit* which are capable of higher cutting speeds than the normal high-speed tool steels. They are used for machining cast iron, hard steel and non-metallic materials such as plastics. Due to the high cost, cemented carbide tools usually consist of a carbide tip or insert brazed on to a steel holder or shank.

STELLITES

These are cobalt-base cast alloys containing elements such as chromium, tungsten and carbon. The structure is usually one of complex carbides in a cobalt and chromium matrix. They are used for tool tips, valves and valve seatings.

MAGNETIC ALLOYS

Magnetic alloys may be roughly divided into two classes according to whether or not they retain their magnetism. The former are referred to as magnetically 'hard' materials and are used for permanent magnets, whilst the latter are said to be magnetically 'soft' and are used for transformer cores, motor and generator armatures and other electrical equipment. A general connection exists between magnetic hardness and mechanical hardness. Treatments which increase mechanical hardness usually increase magnetic hardness.

PERMANENT-MAGNET ALLOYS

The earliest permanent-magnet alloy was the 1% carbon steel in the hardened condition. This was followed by the 6% tungsten steel and the 3–6% chromium steels. In 1920 Honda in Japan introduced a series of permanent-magnet alloys containing 3–35% cobalt with superior properties. These represent the limit of development for quenched martensitic steels.

In 1931 a new era in permanent-magnet alloys began with the development by Mishima in Japan of alloys containing nickel, aluminium and iron. These alloys, in common with the later alloys, undergo precipitation-hardening when tempered at 600°C. after air-cooling from 1,200°C. Development of such alloys, to which the name

Material	*Approximate composition*					BH max. $\times 10^{-6}$ Gauss Oersteds
Martensitic steels						
Carbon steel	1% C					0·18
Chromium steel	1% C + 3·5% Cr					0·29
Tungsten steel	1% C + 6% W					0·30
3% Cobalt	1% C + 3% Co + 7% Cr					0·35
6% Cobalt	1% C + 6% Co + 7% Cr					0·44
15% Cobalt	1% C + 15% Co + 9% Cr					0·62
35% Cobalt	1% C + 35% Co + 5% Cr					0·95
Precipitation-hardening alloys	Al	Ni	Co	Cu	Ti	
Alni	13	24		3·5	Sometimes small additions	1·25
Alnico	10	18	12	6		1·70
Alcomax II	8	11	24	6		4·3
Ticonal	8	14	24	3		5·0
Alnico V	8	14	24	3		4·5
Columax	8	14	23	3		6·8

Table 8.1. Permanent Magnet Alloys

Alni (Table 8.1) was given, was continued in this country by the Permanent Magnet Association Ltd. The addition of cobalt and copper gave rise to the *Alnico* series of alloys which were developed in Sheffield. Alloys such as *Alcomax, Ticonal* and *Alnico V* possess directional or anisotropic properties obtained by placing the alloy in a strong magnetic field during the hardening treatment. Alcomax magnets can be cooled during casting in such a way that their columnar crystals are developed in the same direction as the preferred axis of magnetization. This type of alloy is known commercially as *Columax* and represents the most effective type of permanent magnet alloy available, based on the criterion of the value of the product BH maximum.

HIGH PERMEABILITY ALLOYS

Magnetically soft materials should be readily demagnetized and retain as little magnetism as possible. Such alloys must have a high magnetic permeability, and must absorb a minimum of energy in an alternating magnetic field such as that experienced by a transformer core.

The earliest alloy used for this purpose was soft iron, followed by the iron-silicon alloys containing up to 4·5% silicon. Silicon iron is usually manufactured in the form of dead soft sheet for transformer core laminations. It is rolled and annealed so as to obtain grain growth which assists in obtaining the desired magnetic properties. Preferred orientation of the grains in the direction of rolling can be achieved by alternate cold rolling and annealing. This gives rise to

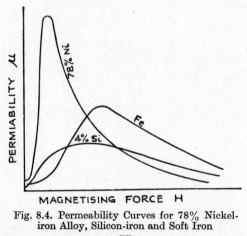

Fig. 8.4. Permeability Curves for 78% Nickel-
iron Alloy, Silicon-iron and Soft Iron

superior magnetic properties in the sheet in the direction of rolling. Nickel-iron alloys such as *Permalloy* (78·5% Ni) and *Mumetal* (75% Ni) are noted for their high magnetic permeability in weak magnetic fields (Fig. 8.4). They are used as shields for submarine cables and for transformer cores.

9. Cast Iron

Cast iron consists basically of pig iron which has been remelted and cast, either alone, or blended with scrap iron or steel. Its melting point (approximately 1,150°–1,250°C.) is lower than that of steel and, in consequence, it can be more readily and cheaply melted, usually in a cupola furnace. The molten metal is very fluid and has the ability to take good casting impressions.

Like steel it always contains the five elements carbon, silicon, manganese, sulphur and phosphorus, but in larger proportions than exist in steel. A typical range of composition for cast iron is $C = 2 \cdot 8 – 3 \cdot 6\%$, $Si = 1 \cdot 0 – 3 \cdot 0\%$, $Mn = 0 \cdot 4 – 1 \cdot 0\%$, $S = 0 \cdot 1 – 0 \cdot 35\%$, $P = 0 \cdot 05 – 1 \cdot 0\%$.

WHITE AND GREY CAST IRONS

The carbon in cast iron may exist in two forms, namely:

1. Combined carbon or cementite, Fe_3C
2. Free carbon or graphite formed by the breakdown of the cementite as follows:

$$Fe_3C \longrightarrow Fe + C$$
$$\text{(CEMENTITE)} \qquad \text{(FERRITE)} \qquad \text{(GRAPHITE)}$$

If the carbon is combined as cementite, the iron will be hard, brittle and unmachinable. A white fracture is apparent when the iron is broken, hence the name *white cast iron.*

If the carbon is free, in the form of graphite, the iron will be relatively soft and machinable and will give a greyish fracture (*grey cast iron*).

If only about half of the cementite has broken down into graphite the iron is referred to as *mottled iron*, due to the mottled appearance of its fracture.

The factors affecting the form of the carbon in cast iron are:

1. THE RATE OF COOLING
2. THE CHEMICAL COMPOSITION
3. SUBSEQUENT HEAT TREATMENT

1. THE RATE OF COOLING

A high cooling rate tends to stabilize the cementite, giving a hard white iron, whereas a slow cooling rate assists the formation of graphite, thus producing a grey iron. The cooling rate will depend upon the section thickness and the type of mould used.

In castings of varying cross-section the thinner sections may consist of white iron and will be harder than the thicker sections, which will consist of grey iron. The cooling rate would be slower in a sand mould than that obtained in a metal mould.

2. CHEMICAL COMPOSITION

(a) *CARBON* lowers the melting point as indicated by the iron-carbon diagram and increases the amount of graphite in the iron.

	White cast iron	*Grey cast iron*
The form of carbon	Combined as Cementite	Free carbon or Graphite
Chemical composition	Low silicon, high sulphur	High silicon, low sulphur
Cooling Rate in mould	Fast	Slow
Properties	Hard, brittle, unmachinable. B.H.N. = 400–500	Relatively soft and machinable. B.H.N. = 180–240
Typical uses	Ploughshares, chilled rolls, balls, stamp shoes, dies and wearing plates. Manufacture of malleable C.I.	Ingot moulds, automobile cylinders and pistons. Machine castings, water main pipes.

Table 9.1. White and Grey Cast Irons

(*b*) *SILICON* aids the formation of graphite and thus tends to produce a grey iron.

(*c*) *SULPHUR*. The direct effect of sulphur is to stabilize the cementite, thus producing a white iron.

(*d*) *MANGANESE* combines with the sulphur to form manganese sulphide and thus indirectly aids the formation of graphite by its effect on the sulphur. However, the direct effect of manganese is to stabilize the cementite. This will occur only if the amount of Mn is greater than that required to combine with the sulphur (1 part S to 1·72 parts Mn).

(*e*) *PHOSPHORUS* has no effect on the form of the carbon in cast iron. It does, however, improve the fluidity by the formation of a low-melting-point phosphide eutectic ($Fe-Fe_3C-Fe_3P$, melting point 960°C.).

3. SUBSEQUENT HEAT-TREATMENT

White-iron castings can be graphitized by an annealing treatment, as in the manufacture of malleable cast iron (dealt with later).

The distinction between grey and white cast irons may be summarized as in Table 9.1.

THE STRUCTURE OF GREY CAST IRONS

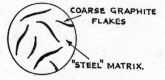

Fig. 9.1. Grey Cast Iron

Structurally, grey cast irons may be considered as being composed of a 'steel' matrix and coarse flakes of graphite (Fig. 9.1). The 'steel' matrix, usually pearlitic, has an ultimate tensile strength of approximately 50 tons per square inch, yet ordinary grey cast iron has an U.T.S. of only 12–15 tons per square inch, with very little shock resistance. This can be attributed to the presence of the graphite flakes, which have no strength, and act in the same way as cracks with sharp edges. This gives rise to points of stress concentration which decrease shock resistance and strength.

The strength of grey cast iron can, therefore, be increased in one of two ways, either by modifying the form of the graphite so as to eliminate its weakening effect, or by strengthening the 'steel' matrix. Using the first method, the presence of coarse flakes of graphite is avoided in the manufacture of malleable, inoculated and spheroidal graphite cast irons (Fig. 9.2), whilst the strength of the 'steel' matrix may best be increased by the addition of alloying elements.

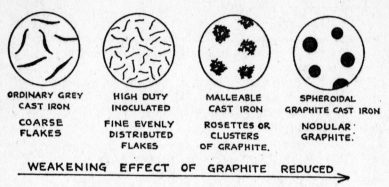

ORDINARY GREY CAST IRON   HIGH DUTY INOCULATED   MALLEABLE CAST IRON   SPHEROIDAL GRAPHITE CAST IRON

COARSE FLAKES   FINE EVENLY DISTRIBUTED FLAKES   ROSETTES OR CLUSTERS OF GRAPHITE.   NODULAR GRAPHITE.

WEAKENING EFFECT OF GRAPHITE REDUCED →

Fig. 9.2. Form of the Graphite in Various Grey Irons

MALLEABLE CAST IRON

Malleable cast iron is made by the annealing of white iron castings. Two processes are used, namely the *WHITEHEART PROCESS* (developed in Europe) and the *BLACKHEART PROCESS* (developed in the U.S.A.) (Table 9.2).

The disadvantages of malleable cast iron are the length of time involved in the process, and the fact that the process is limited to small sections (usually less than 2 in.), since a white iron has to be produced initially.

Uses

Malleable iron is used for small structural components for automobiles, machine tools, agricultural machines, gas and oil burners, pipe fittings and plumbing supplies.

INOCULATED HIGH-DUTY CAST IRON

Castings with the graphite in a fine evenly distributed flake form can be produced by the addition of a small amount of graphitizing element, e.g. silicon, in the form of calcium silicide or ferro-silicon. The composition of the molten iron is such that it would normally produce a white iron. The inoculent is added at the spout of the cupola. The effect of inoculation disappears upon remelting. A

	Whiteheart	*Blackheart*
Process	White iron castings are packed in hematite iron ore in boxes. Annealed at 950°C. for 4–6 days.	White iron castings embedded in a neutral packing, e.g. sand or crushed slag. Annealed at 850°–900°C. for 3–4 days.
Composition of white iron castings used	C = 3·00–3·60 Si = 0·3–1·0 Mn = 0·2–0·6 S = 0·15–0·40 P = 0·08% max.	C = 1·75–2·7 Si = 0·6–1·30 Mn = 0·4% max. S = 0·07–0·12 P = 0·20% max.
Microstructure	 Clusters of graphite in a ferrite-pearlite matrix	 Clusters of graphite in a ferrite matrix. Rather more graphite than in whiteheart iron
Mechanical properties U.T.S. % Elongation Angle of Bend B.H.N. Izod value	 22–28 5–10 90° 120–200 10–20	 22–25 12–18 180° 110–120 14–16

Table 9.2. Malleable Cast Iron

typical example of an inoculated cast iron is *Meehanite*, which possesses an U.T.S. of 21–24 t.s.i. The matrix structure is entirely pearlitic.

SPHEROIDAL GRAPHITE CAST IRON

Castings with the graphite in nodular form can be obtained by adding a small amount of magnesium, in the form of nickel-magnesium alloy, to the ladle before casting. The alloy addition is of the order of 2%. The composition of the molten iron is such that it would normally cast white.

There are two main types of S.G. iron, namely cast and annealed.

	Cast	*Annealed*
Microstructure	PEARLITE + GRAPHITE Above 2 in. thick a pearlite-ferrite matrix is possible	FERRITE + GRAPHITE Annealed at 900°C. for a few hours followed by controlled cooling
Mechanical properties U.T.S. % Elongation Compressive strength B.H.N. Izod Value	35–45 1–5 65–80 230–280 4	27–35* 10–25 45–58 140–180 12

* Annealed S.G. cast iron shows a well-defined yield point on the stress-strain curve.

Table 9.3. S.G. Cast Iron

Applications

The present and possible applications of S.G. iron are numerous. Its use enables section thickness, and consequently weight, to be reduced. Toughness and ductility can be obtained in castings which are too thick for malleabilizing. Such irons can replace steel castings and forgings. Applications include cast crankshafts, agricultural and marine castings, heavy machinery frames, hand tools, gas and water pipes.

ALLOY CAST IRONS

The chief elements alloyed with cast iron are nickel, chromium, copper and molybdenum. Of these, nickel is the most important and its effects may be summarized as follows:

1. It aids the formation of graphite. In this respect, it is approximately one-third as effective as silicon.

2. It has a grain-refining effect. More uniform properties are therefore obtained in castings of varying cross-section since nickel prevents the formation of a coarse grain in thick sections, whilst preventing the formation of a hard white iron in the thinner sections.

3. It lowers the critical cooling rate and the critical range. Progressive increases in nickel content change the microstructure of the matrix from pearlite to martensite to austenite.

The pearlitic alloy cast irons contain up to about 2% nickel, and are used for general engineering castings, whilst the hard martensitic irons, e.g. *Ni-Hard* (4·5 Ni 1·5 Cr), are used for wear-resisting castings. The austenitic cast irons are all non-magnetic, and possess good heat and corrosion resistance, and high coefficients of expansion and of electrical resistance. Typical examples are:

Trade name	T.C.	Ni	Cr	Si	Other elements
'Ni-Resist'	2·8	14	2	1·6	6% Cu
'No-Mag'	2·8	11	–	1	6% Mn
'Nicrosilal'	2·0	18	2	5	–

Table 9.4. Compositions of some Typical Austenitic Alloy Cast Irons

GROWTH OF CAST IRON

When cast iron is heated and cooled through the range 700°–800°C. the cementite in the pearlite breaks down to form ferrite and graphite, thus producing an increase in volume. Subsequently hot gases penetrate into the minute cavities formed and oxidize the ferrite, giving a further increase in volume. This gives rise to stresses which may cause warping and characteristic crazy-cracking at the surface. Irons such as *Nicrosilal* (Table 9.4) have been developed to resist growth.

10. Copper and its Alloys

Copper is widely used industrially due mainly to its high electrical and thermal conductivity, good corrosion resistance and workability. It is employed extensively in the electrical industry for conductors of all kinds. It is also used in chemical plant construction and in the building industry for such applications as domestic water pipes and roofing.

There are many grades of commercial copper available, e.g.

1. Tough-pitch Copper (containing 0·05% oxygen)

When tough-pitch copper is heated above 400°C. in reducing atmospheres it is liable to a defect known as 'gassing'. The hydrogen or carbon monoxide penetrates into the metal and reacts with the cuprous oxide present to form steam. The steam produced is unable to escape and builds up a pressure which forces individual grains apart, forming intercrystalline fissures. The ductility of the metal is considerably reduced. Such conditions may be realized during gas welding, and deoxidized copper is usually specified for welding purposes.

2. Deoxidized Copper

Copper is usually deoxidized with phosphorus which has a higher affinity for oxygen than has copper. Deoxidized copper, although more suitable for welding, usually contains 0·05% phosphorus as a residual deoxidant which reduces the electrical conductivity.

3. O.F.H.C. Copper

Oxygen-free high conductivity (O.F.H.C.) copper contains neither oxygen nor residual deoxidant and therefore possesses a high

G

electrical conductivity. It is made by melting and casting electrolytically refined copper in a non-oxidizing atmosphere.

4. Arsenical Copper

0·3–0·5% arsenic may be added to deoxidized or tough-pitch copper to improve the resistance to scaling at elevated temperatures. Arsenical copper is used for locomotive fireboxes, boiler tubes, stay-bolts and rivets.

5. Free-machining Copper

Approximately 0·5% selenium or tellurium may be added to copper to improve machinability. These elements do not greatly decrease the electrical conductivity which is usually about 95% that of pure copper.

The mechanical properties of the various grades of copper do not vary very much. Copper is soft and ductile and capable of a considerable degree of cold-work. Typical mechanical properties in the cold-worked and annealed condition are:

0·1% P.S.	U.T.S.	% EL	V.P.N.
4	14	55	45

COPPER ALLOYS

The more important copper-base alloys may be classified as follows:
- (a) COPPER-ZINC (BRASSES)
- (b) COPPER-TIN (TIN BRONZES)
- (c) COPPER-TIN-PHOSPHORUS (PHOSPHOR-BRONZES)
- (d) COPPER-ALUMINIUM (ALUMINIUM BRONZES)
- (e) COPPER-NICKEL (CUPRO-NICKELS)

The study of these alloys is to some extent simplified by a similarity in the microstructures. The initial solid solution produced by the addition of an alloying element is represented by the symbol α. The α solid solution is always soft and ductile and has the same type of microstructure in all the alloys. When the limit of solid solubility has been exceeded the β constituent appears in the microstructure, and this structure is associated with increased strength at the expense of ductility. Further addition of alloying element results in the formation of hard brittle constituents represented by the symbols γ and δ.

THE BRASSES

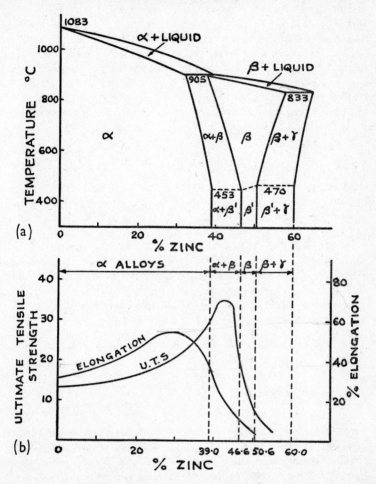

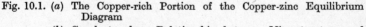

Fig. 10.1. (a) The Copper-rich Portion of the Copper-zinc Equilibrium Diagram

(b) Graph to show Relationship between Microstructure and Mechanical Properties of the Brasses

Reference to the copper-zinc thermal equilibrium diagram Fig. 10.1(a) shows that the soft α solid solution exists in alloys containing 0–39% zinc. Alloys containing 39–46·6% zinc have a microstructure consisting of $\alpha+\beta$, whilst those containing 46·6–50·6% zinc consist entirely of the β constituent. Brasses with more than 50·6% zinc contain the brittle γ constituent and such alloys are not commercially important.

The change from β to β^1 which occurs between 453°–470°C. (Fig. 10.1(a)) is not important to the engineer and the symbol β will be used to describe the room temperature β^1 structure.

The relationship between zinc content, microstructure and mechanical properties is shown in Fig. 10.1(b). It is apparent that for maximum ductility an alloy containing 30% zinc should be employed. The optimum combination of strength and ductility is obtained in an alloy containing about 40% zinc. These two alloys form the basis of the chief industrial brasses.

1. 70:30 BRASS (a brass)

Cold-working brass used for cold-rolled sheets, wire drawing, deep drawing, pressing and in tube manufacture. It is frequently known as *cartridge brass* because of its use in the manufacture of cartridge cases.

In the cast state the alloy consists of a cored structure of the a solid solution. Annealing after cold-work produces a twinned crystal structure (Fig. 10·3(a)). This type of structure is characteristic of face-centred cubic alloys in this condition. Typical mechanical properties of 70:30 brass in the cold-worked and annealed condition are as follows:

0·1% P.S.	U.T.S.	EL	V.P.N.
5	21	70	65

Improvement in corrosion resistance can be obtained by the addition of tin or aluminium, and alloys such as aluminium brass (76:22:2 Cu:Zn:Al) and Admiralty brass (70:29:1 Cu:Zn:Sn) are used for marine condensers and other heat-exchange equipment.

2. 60:40 BRASS (aβ brass)

Suitable for hot-working by rolling, extrusion and stamping and for the manufacture of castings. This type of brass is frequently known as *Muntz metal* as it was developed by G. F. Muntz.

In the cast state the microstructure is of a Widmanstatten type, Fig. 10.3(b), with a at the grain boundaries and along the crystal planes of the β constituent. Hot-working refines the structure giving a more uniform distribution of α in a matrix of β (Fig. 10.3 (c)). Typical mechanical properties of 60:40 brass are as follows:

Condition	0·1% P.S.	U.T.S.	EL	V.P.N.
Cast	6	18–23	25–50	60–70
Hot rolled	6–15	20–30	25–40	75–150

Approximately 2–3½% lead is frequently added to brasses of this type to improve machinability. Lead is insoluble in the brass and appears as small globules in the microstructure which cause the machining chips to break up into small pieces.

3. HIGH-TENSILE BRASSES

These are essentially brasses of the 60:40 type which contain additional elements such as manganese, aluminium, tin, iron and nickel. These 'high-tensile' brasses may be used in the cast or wrought state for applications where strength coupled with a good corrosion resistance is required. Applications include marine propellers, autoclaves, pump rods and shafts, pickling crates, stampings and pressings for automobile fittings and switch-gear. Typical compositions and mechanical properties of high-tensile brasses are shown in the following table.

B.S.1400	Cu min.	Mn max.	Al max.	Fe max.	Sn max.	Ni max.	Microstructure	U.T.S. min.	EL min.
H.T.B 2–C	55	3	5	0·5-2·0	0·5	2	$\alpha+\beta$*	38	15
H.T.B 3–C	55	4	3–6	1·0-2·5	0·2	1	β	48	12

* Area of α constituent = 15% minimum.

The separate effects of added elements on the properties of brasses are as follows:

Tin improves the corrosion resistance of the brass but should not exceed 1% owing to the formation of a hard brittle constituent. Tin is present in naval brass (61:38:1 Cu:Zn:Sn) for this purpose.

Iron forms a complex bluish iron-rich constituent when present in amounts greater than 0·35%. This constituent provides nuclei for crystallization and thus has a grain-refining effect in castings.

Manganese is often added up to 2% in the high-tensile brass known as 'manganese bronze'. Its principal effect is that of a deoxidant, producing sounder castings and improving the tensile strength.

Aluminium greatly increases the tensile strength and the corrosion resistance of the brass. It reduces zinc losses during melting by forming a protective film of aluminium oxide on the surface of the molten alloy. This film can, however, provide difficulties in casting and soldering.

Nickel has only a slight effect on mechanical properties and its main function is to increase corrosion and erosion resistance. It is therefore present in manganese-bronze for marine propellers.

THE TIN BRONZES

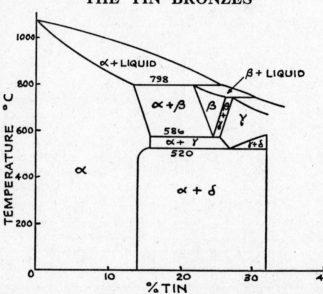

Fig. 10.2. The Copper-rich Portion of the Copper-tin Equilibrium Diagram

Reference to Fig. 10.2 reveals that at room temperatures up to 14% tin can dissolve in copper to form the α solid solution. However, in practice the brittle δ constituent appears with 7% tin in sand castings and with 5% in chill castings. The commercial bronzes rarely contain more than 15% tin so that the microstructure of these alloys will consist of either:

(1) Soft α constituent alone

or (2) Hard (α + δ) eutectoid in a soft α matrix. The main types of commercial tin-bronze are as follows:

1. COINAGE BRONZE (α bronze) 95:4:1 Cu:Sn:Zn

The zinc is present mainly as a deoxidizer. The alloy is soft and ductile and in the cold-worked and annealed condition will consist of twinned crystals of the α solid solution. The alloy is the standard British 'copper' coinage.

2. ADMIRALTY GUN-METAL 88:10:2 Cu:Sn:Zn

Zinc is present as a deoxidizer and also increases the fluidity of the casting. In the cast state the alloy consists of the hard $(\alpha + \delta)$ eutectoid in a cored α matrix (Fig. 10.3(d)). Due to the presence of the eutectoid it cannot be cold-worked but may be hot-worked above 590°C. Admiralty gun-metal is used chiefly for castings requiring strength combined with a good corrosion resistance, e.g. high-pressure steam and water fittings. The microstructure of hard particles in a soft matrix gives the alloy good bearing properties. Typical mechanical properties are as follows:

Condition	0·1% P.S.	U.T.S.	EL	V.P.N.
Sand cast	8	16–22	12–20	70–100

This is not a good alloy for producing pressure-tight castings but can be improved by the addition of 1% Pb without loss of strength. It is not recommended for use at temperatures above 450°F.

Gun-metals have been developed where lead has replaced the more expensive tin with certain advantages. The 85:5:5:5 Cu:Sn:Zn-Pb alloy (BS 1400 LG2) has moderate strength at room temperatures but possesses excellent pressure tightness. It is superior to other gun-metals for use at temperatures in the region 450°–550°F. The 86:7:5:2: Cu:Sn:Zn:Pb alloy (BS 1400 LG3) has little advantage over the 85-5-5-5 alloy as regards strength and is considerably inferior for pressure tightness.

The addition of nickel to leaded gun-metals has led to the development of the 86:6·5:3:3·5:2 Cu:Sn:Zn:Pb:Ni alloy by the Mond Nickel Co., Ltd. Castings in this leaded gun-metal have mechanical properties equivalent to 88:10:2 combined with the castability and pressure tightness of 85:5:5:5 gun-metal and they are less sensitive to the effect of variations in casting section.

3. 15% TIN-BRONZE ALLOY

The cast 15% tin-bronze is suitable for use as a bearing alloy, since it consists of hard particles of $(\alpha + \delta)$ eutectoid in a soft α matrix. When the alloy is water quenched from about 600°C. the structure consists of $\alpha + \beta$ and in this condition it is used for bells, since the tougher β constituent gives a better tone.

(a) 70:30 BRASS, COLD WORKED AND ANNEALED CONDITION. TWINNED CRYSTALS OF THE α SOLID SOLUTION.

(b) 60:40 BRASS, CAST CONDITION. LIGHT FLAKES OF α SOLID SOLUTION IN A MATRIX OF DARK β CONSTITUENTS.

(c) 60:40 BRASS, HOT WORKED. (TRANSVERSE SECTION.) LIGHT ISLANDS OF α SOLID SOLUTION IN A DARK MATRIX OF THE β CONSTITUENT.

(d) ADMIRALTY GUNMETAL 88:10:2. Cu:Sn:Zn. CAST CONDITION. ISLANDS OF $(\alpha + \delta)$ EUTECTOID IN A CORED MATRIX OF THE α SOLID SOLUTION.

Fig. 10.3. Typical Microstructures of Copper-base Alloys

Lead is frequently added to tin-bronzes to improve machinability (0·5–1·0%) and bearing qualities (5–15%). Leaded bronzes for bearings will be discussed in Chapter 12.

PHOSPHOR-BRONZE ALLOYS

The phosphor-bronze alloys are tin-bronzes containing small amounts of phosphorus, consequently they may be studied with reference to the copper-tin equilibrium diagram. Two distinct types of phosphor-bronze may be recognized, viz. (1) *wrought* and (2) *cast phosphor-bronze*, as shown in the following table:

	Wrought Phosphor-Bronzes	Cast Phosphor-Bronzes
Range of composition	3·0–8·5% Sn 0·1–0·3% P	9·0–13·0% Sn 0·3–1·0% P
Microstructure	α In the cold worked and annealed condition twinned crystals are revealed	α + (α + δ) Plates of the hard constituent Cu_3P (copper phosphide) may be associated with the eutectoid
Typical Mechanical Properties	P.S. = 8–10 U.T.S. = 22–24 % EL = 65 V.P.N. = 75	P.S. = 8–10 U.T.S. = 14–20 % EL = 3–15 V.P.N. = 70–110
Uses	Instrument springs Steam turbine blading	Bearings

ALUMINIUM-BRONZES

The aluminium-bronze alloys are finding increasing application due to a useful combination of properties. These alloys are capable of heat-treatment in a similar manner to plain carbon steels, and in the wrought heat-treated condition a high tensile strength coupled with good ductility is obtained. Aluminium-bronzes possess good working properties, wear, fatigue and corrosion resistance. Certain difficulties are met, however, in the production of these alloys due to the formation of hard tenacious oxide films on the surface of the molten alloy. Special casting procedures have to be adopted so as to avoid turbulence, and to prevent the oxide entering the casting forming brittle films. The same difficulties were also obtained in fusion welding, but these have largely been overcome and satisfactory arc welding of aluminium-bronzes is possible.

The portion of the copper-aluminium diagram relevant to the aluminium-bronzes is shown in Fig. 10.4.

Alloys containing up to 9·4% aluminium consist of the soft ductile α solid solution. The γ_2 constituent is hard and brittle and therefore industrial aluminium-bronzes rarely contain more than 10% aluminium.

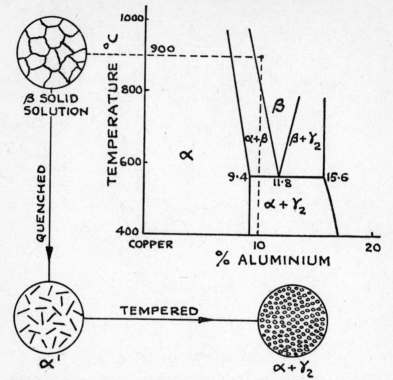

Fig. 10.4. Portion of the Copper-aluminium Diagram illustrating Structural Changes occurring during Heat-treatment of the 10% Aluminium-bronze Alloy

Two main types of aluminium-bronze are employed:

1. WROUGHT ALPHA ALLOY

This contains 5–7% aluminium, and may be readily hot- or cold-worked. In the cold-worked and annealed condition the microstructure will consist of twinned crystals of the α solid solution, similar to Fig. 10.3(a).

The 5% aluminium alloy, due to its colour, is used for imitation jewellery and for decorative purposes, whereas the 7% alloy containing other elements such as nickel, iron and manganese is used for the tubes of marine condensers and other heat exchangers.

2. 10% ALUMINIUM-BRONZE ALLOY

This is the most important alloy and is used both for castings and in the hot-worked condition. When the alloy is slowly cooled the microstructure consists of dendrites of the α solid solution in a coarse eutectoid matrix $(\alpha + \gamma_2)$. The presence of this coarse eutectoid embrittles the alloy and this defect known as 'self-annealing' may be overcome by the addition of 1–3% iron which refines the structure or by heat-treatment. The finer eutectoid obtained in chill cast iron-containing castings resembles the β constituent in other copper-base alloys.

The usual heat-treatment for a 10% aluminium-bronze alloy is as follows:

1. Water quenching from 900°C.
2. Tempering at 550°–650°C.

The effect of heat-treatment on the microstructure of the alloy is shown in Fig. 10.4. The changes taking place are analogous to those occurring in the plain carbon steels. At 900°C. the alloy consists of a uniform solid solution β (analogous to austenite). Water quenching from this temperature results in a hard needle-like constituent referred to as α^1 (analogous to martensite). Tempering at 550°–650°C. results in the precipitation of fine particles to give a tough structure of $\alpha + \gamma_2$ (analogous to sorbite). Typical mechanical properties in the hot-worked and fully heat-treated condition are as follows:

U.T.S.	EL	B.H.N.
40–45	30–40	170–180

The 10% aluminium-bronze alloy may also contain additions of iron (up to 5%), nickel (up to 5%) and manganese (up to 2·5%). These complex aluminium-bronzes may be used as castings or in the hot-worked condition. In hot-worked condition a tensile strength of up to 50 tons per sq. in. can be obtained with 15–25% elongation.

Aluminium-bronze alloys are used in the marine and chemical industries for applications where strength coupled with a good corrosion resistance is important, e.g. propellers, propeller shafts, pump castings, pickling crates, chains and hooks. They are being increasingly used as non-sparking tools.

COPPER-NICKEL ALLOYS

Copper and nickel form a complete series of solid solutions (Fig. 10.5). In the cast state the alloys will exhibit coring which can be removed by annealing. All the alloys may be fabricated by hot- and cold-working. Annealing after cold-working may be carried out between 550°–750°C.

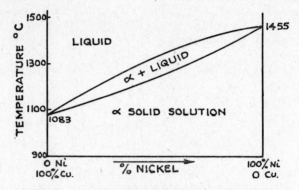

Fig. 10.5. The Copper-nickel Equilibrium Diagram

The copper-rich alloys known as the *cupro-nickels* are extremely malleable and are capable of cold-work without intermediate annealing. The 80:20 and 70:30 cupro-nickels are used for condenser tubes, whilst the 75:25 alloy is used for the present-day British 'silver' coinage.

Typical mechanical properties of the cupro-nickel alloys in the annealed condition are as follows:

U.T.S.	*EL*	*B.H.N.*
22–25	40–45	75–80

COPPER-BERYLLIUM ALLOY

The copper-beryllium alloy containing 2% beryllium and up to 0·5% cobalt exhibits the property of precipitation—hardening to a marked degree. This phenomenon will be discussed in more detail in Chapter 14.

Quenching from 800°C. produces a soft supersaturated solid solution. This can be hardened by cold-work, and tempering at 300°–320°C. hardens both the soft and work-hardened alloy.

The combined effect of work hardening and precipitation or temper-hardening gives the following typical mechanical properties:

L.P.	U.T.S.	EL	B.H.N.
48	90	2	365

These alloys are characterized by a high fatigue limit and good elastic properties, and are used for springs, bellows, diaphragms for pressure recording instruments and non-sparking tools.

11. The Light Alloys

ALUMINIUM

Aluminium is extracted from the mineral bauxite, which consists mainly of aluminium oxide, by an electrolytic process. The process, developed simultaneously by Hall in the U.S.A. and Heroult in France in 1886, involves the electrolysis of a solution of bauxite in fused cryolite. The purity of the aluminium produced is about 99·5%, but this can be raised to about 99·99% by further refining.

One of the most important characteristics of aluminium is its lightness. The specific gravity is 2·7 compared with 7·8 for mild steel. A high strength:weight ratio is therefore obtained in heat-treated aluminium alloys which makes them suitable for use in the aircraft and automobile industries. The thermal conductivity of aluminium is about five times that of mild steel and this property, together with that of lightness, makes the metal suitable for pistons and connecting rods of internal combustion engines. The electrical conductivity of aluminium is about 60% that of copper, but weight for weight it is better than copper. It is therefore used for cable work, provided a central core of thin steel wire is used as reinforcement. Aluminium has a high affinity for oxygen and readily forms a thin hard self-healing film of aluminium oxide on its surface. This protective surface film, which is only about 5×10^{-7} in. in thickness, accounts for the good corrosion resistance of aluminium. It is particularly resistant to concentrated nitric acid, but not to alkalies, which dissolve the film. Aluminium and its alloys are therefore used in chemical plant construction, marine superstructures, food containers and wrappers, cooking utensils and aluminium paints.

Commercially pure aluminium is soft and weak. In the annealed state it exhibits a tensile strength of about 5 tons per sq. in., elongation of 35% and Brinell hardness of 23. It is therefore unsuitable for most engineering purposes. The mechanical properties can be improved by alloying, the chief alloying elements being copper, silicon, manganese, magnesium, zinc and nickel.

ALUMINIUM ALLOYS

Aluminium alloys are available under a considerable number of trade names which can be very confusing. For general engineering purposes aluminium alloys are covered by British Standards 1470–77 (wrought forms) and 1490 (ingots and castings). Aircraft materials are covered by the 'L' series of British Standards and the D.T.D. Specifications. The latter are issued by the Directorate of Technical Development, Ministry of Supply. Aluminium alloys may be conveniently classified as follows:

1. WROUGHT ALLOYS (*a*) NOT HEAT-TREATED
   (*b*) HEAT-TREATED
2. CAST ALLOYS (*a*) NOT HEAT-TREATED
   (*b*) HEAT-TREATED

1(*a*) WROUGHT ALLOYS (NOT HEAT-TREATED)

The chief alloys in this class are the $1\frac{1}{4}\%$ manganese alloy and those containing 2–7% magnesium. They are strengthened only by cold-working and are available in various tempers, e.g. 'soft', 'half hard', 'three-quarter hard', etc. Softening may be carried out by annealing at 350°–400°C. These alloys are characterized by good corrosion resistance. The magnesium-containing alloys are particularly resistant to sea-water corrosion, and are therefore used for many ship-building applications. The $1\frac{1}{4}\%$ manganese alloy is used extensively for roofing sheets, wall cladding for various buildings and food containers. Typical mechanical properties for a 5% magnesium alloy are as follows:

Specification	Composition	Condition	0·1% P.S.	U.T.S.	EL
B.S.1470N.S.6	5% Mg	Soft	7	17	20
		Half hard	18	21	6

1(*b*) WROUGHT ALLOYS (HEAT-TREATED)

The alloys in this group are capable of being hardened and strengthened by a process known as 'age-hardening'. The usual alloying elements are copper, magnesium, manganese, silicon and zinc. The phenomenon of age-hardening will be discussed with reference to alloys containing 4% copper, which is the basic composition of alloys of the Duralumin type. The aluminium-rich portion of the aluminium-copper diagram is shown in Fig. 11.1.

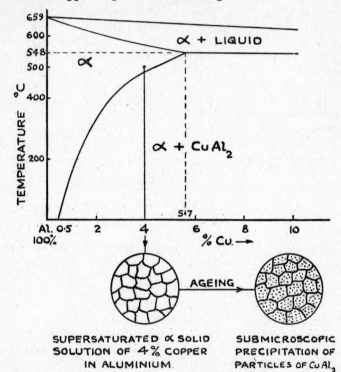

Fig. 11.1. Aluminium-rich Portion of Aluminium-copper Equilibrium Diagram illustrating the Age-hardening Treatment of an Alloy containing 4% Copper

At room temperatures the solubility of copper in aluminium to form the a solid solution is only 0·5%. The solid solubility increases with temperature reaching a maximum of 5·7% at 548°C. Upon slow cooling from the a region a 4% copper alloy will precipitate coarse particles of the compound $CuAl_2$. In this condition the alloy will be relatively weak and brittle.

The full age-hardening treatment involves three distinct stages:

1. Heating the alloy to a prescribed temperature (e.g. 500°C.) to dissolve all the copper and any other alloying element.

2. Quenching from this temperature to preserve the a solid solution at room temperatures. These two treatments are referred to as *solution treatment*.

102

3. Ageing. Hardening may now occur spontaneously at room temperatures when it is referred to as 'natural ageing'. Natural ageing may be delayed after solution treatment by storing the work in a refrigerator at $-6°$ to $-10°C$. This is important where riveting and pressing operations are involved and delays are likely to occur. In some alloys ageing is carried out by reheating the alloy up to 150°–170°C. for a few hours, when it is referred to as 'artificial ageing' or 'precipitation-hardening'. With such alloys the time and temperature of ageing differ with each alloy and must be closely controlled to give optimum results.

No complete explanation of age-hardening has yet been given, but the precipitation of fine particles of compounds such as $CuAl_2$ and Mg_2Si appears to play an important part. Maximum hardness occurs, however, before a precipitate can be detected microscopically.

The original Duralumin alloy has an approximate composition of 4% copper with 0·5% each of magnesium, manganese, silicon and iron. The last two elements are strictly impurities in the alloy. The heat-treatment of this alloy involves solution treatment at 490°–500°C. followed by natural ageing for four days. In the fully aged condition typical mechanical properties are as follows:

0·1% P.S.	U.T.S.	EL	B.H.N.
15	25	15	110

The alloy is used in the form of bars, tubes, sheet, forgings, rivets for general purposes and stressed parts in aircraft.

The addition of controlled amounts of silicon up to a maximum of 0·9% produces a higher strength Duralumin-type alloy (H.15) used extensively for highly stressed parts in aircraft. Typical mechanical properties are as follows:

0·1% P.S.	U.T.S.	EL	B.H.N.
26	30	8	135

These properties are obtained by solution treatment at 510°C. followed by precipitation hardening at 170°C. for about ten hours.

The highest strength alloys are those of the Al-Zn-Mg-Cu type, e.g. D.T.D. 683. A typical composition is approximately 6% Zn, 2·5% Mg and 1·5% Cu. After precipitation-hardening such an alloy would possess an ultimate tensile strength of 35–38 tons per sq. in.

The Al-Mg-Si alloys which contain approximately 1% Mg and 1% Si, but no copper, have a high corrosion resistance but are not as strong as the copper-containing Duralumin alloys.

The wrought heat-treated alloys are frequently protected from corrosion by a layer of pure metal (*Alclad* or *Aldural*). This pure metal cladding is applied by a hot-rolling process (page 136). Clad alloys therefore combine high strength with good corrosion resistance.

2(a) CAST ALLOYS (NOT HEAT-TREATED)

The most important casting alloys are those of the aluminium-silicon type, containing 10–13% silicon. These alloys are characterized by low specific gravity, low shrinkage, high fluidity and pressure tightness. They are suitable for sand castings, and gravity and pressure die castings. The aluminium-rich portion of the aluminium-silicon diagram is shown in Fig. 11.2.

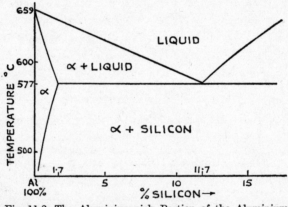

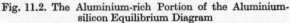

Fig. 11.2. The Aluminium-rich Portion of the Aluminium-silicon Equilibrium Diagram

It will be observed that these alloys are of approximate eutectic composition. The normal mechanical properties of these alloys are greatly improved by a process known as *modification*. This involves the addition of approximately 0·05% sodium to the molten alloy. A considerable refinement of the eutectic structure results with consequent improvement in mechanical properties. Modification can increase the ultimate tensile strength from 8–13 tons per sq. in. and the percentage elongation from 5–15%. Typical mechanical properties are as follows:

B.S.1490	Si%	Condition	0·1% P.S.	U.T.S.	EL	B.H.N.
LM 6	10–13	Sand Cast	3·5–4·0	10·5–12	5–10	50–55
		Chill cast	4·0–4·5	12–15	7–15	55–60

Alloys of this type are known by various trade names, e.g. *Alpax* and *Silumen*.

These alloys possess good corrosion resistance and are suitable for marine castings, automobile fittings, water-cooled manifolds and jackets, thin-section and intricate castings such as motor housings, meter cases and switch boxes, and castings for the dye and chemical industries.

Casting alloys of the Al-Mg-Mn type containing 3–6% Mg and 0·3–0·7% Mn are noted for their high corrosion resistance particularly in marine atmospheres. Such alloys are suitable for sand and gravity die castings. Pressure die castings are possible only in relatively simple shapes.

2(*b*) CAST ALLOYS (HEAT-TREATED)

The heat-treatment of cast alloys is similar to that of the wrought alloys although the times required are generally longer.

The earliest alloy of this type was Y alloy developed during the 1914–18 war as an aero-engine piston alloy. Y alloy conforms to B.S. 1490 LM14 and contains approximately 4% Cu, 2% Ni and 1·5% Mg. The full heat-treatment involves solution treatment at 500°–520°C. for six hours followed by natural ageing for five days or precipitation-hardening for two hours at 100°C. Typical mechanical properties in the chill-cast and fully heat-treated condition are as follows:

0·1% P.S.	U.T.S.	EL	B.H.N
14–16	18–20	1–3	100–130

Y alloy can also be used in the form of forgings, but is chiefly used in the cast form. It retains its strength at elevated temperatures and is used for diesel and high-duty petrol engine pistons and cylinder heads.

The alloy *Lo-Ex* corresponding to B.S. 1490 LM13 is noted for its low thermal expansion and is used for pistons for all types of diesel and petrol engines, and other engine parts operating at elevated temperatures. This alloy is of the 11–13% silicon type and contains approximately 0·9% Cu, 1·2% Mg and 2·5% Ni.

The alloy RR50 is used for sand and gravity die castings for aircraft and road vehicle engines. This alloy can be precipitation-hardened at 150°–175°C. for 8–24 hours without preliminary solution treatment. A typical composition for RR50 together with mechanical properties is as follows:

Cu	Ni	Mg	Fe	Ti	Si	0·1% P.S.	U.T.S.	EL
1·5	1·2	0·15	1·0	0·15	2·5	8	13	3

MAGNESIUM

The development and application of magnesium alloys have increased considerably over the past twenty years. Pure magnesium has poor mechanical properties and is not suitable for engineering applications. This can be overcome by alloying and subsequent working or heat-treatment. The characteristic properties of magnesium and its alloys are as follows:

1. *Lightness*
The specific gravity of magnesium is 1·7 compared with 2·7 for aluminium and 7·5 for steel. Magnesium alloys suitably heat-treated possess a high stiffness-to-weight ratio.

2. *High Affinity for Oxygen and Nitrogen in the Molten Condition*
Special fluxes are necessary to avoid the formation of oxide and nitride inclusions in the metal.

3. *Good Machinability*
Magnesium alloys can be machined faster than other metals, but certain elementary precautions are necessary to eliminate fire risk.

4. *Workability*
Magnesium has a hexagonal close-packed lattice structure. Metals possessing this structure are not readily cold-worked. Magnesium alloys, particularly those containing zirconium, are readily hot-worked in the range 300°–500°C.

5. *Corrosion Resistance*
The resistance to atmospheric corrosion may be considered slightly better than that of mild steel, but protection is usually given by

paint on a chromated surface (page 137). A marked improvement in corrosion resistance is obtained by reducing the iron and nickel contents. The $1\frac{1}{2}\%$ manganese alloy is noted for its good corrosion resistance.

CLASSIFICATION OF MAGNESIUM ALLOYS

Magnesium alloys may be conveniently classified as follows:

    (1) Magnesium—manganese alloys
    (2) Magnesium—aluminium—zinc alloys
    (3) Zirconium-containing alloys.

Magnesium alloys are known under various specifications. In this discussion the alloys will be given the appropriate *Elektron* alloy specification.

1. MAGNESIUM-MANGANESE ALLOYS

E.g. A.M. 503 containing $1\cdot5\%$ Mn. These alloys are used in the wrought condition and possess good corrosion-resistance and weldability. Typical mechanical properties in the form of sheet are as follows:

$0\cdot1\%$ *P.S.*	*U.T.S*	*EL*
5–10	13–18	5–14

2. MAGNESIUM-ALUMINIUM-ZINC ALLOYS

These are used in both the cast and wrought forms. Typical examples are as follows:

Elektron Alloy	*Composition*		*Condition*	$0\cdot1\%$ *P.S.*	*U.T.S.*	*EL*
	Al	*Zn*				
AZ 91	9·5	0·5	Cast + heat-treated	6·5–8·5	13–16·5	1–4
AZM	6·0	1·0	Extruded bars section 3 in.	11–14	17–22	10–18

3. ZIRCONIUM-CONTAINING ALLOYS

The commercial production of zirconium-containing alloys started in 1946. The addition of 0·6–0·7% zirconium gives rise to pronounced grain refinement and improved values of the 0·1% proof stress. The hot-workability of these alloys is particularly good. Zirconium-containing alloys can be used in both the cast and the wrought conditions. Typical examples are as follows:

Elektron Alloy	Composition		Condition	0·1% P.S.	U.T.S.	EL
	Zn	Zr				
Z5Z	4·5	0·7	Cast + heat-treated	8·5–10·5	15–18	5–12
ZW3	3·0	0·7	Press forgings	13–15	19–22	8–14

The addition of thorium and rare-earth elements such as cerium to zirconium-containing alloys greatly improves the creep resistance at elevated temperatures. Examples are ZTI (3% thorium, 2·2% Zn, 0·7% Zr) and ZREI (2·7% rare-earths, 2·2% Zn, 0·6% Zr).

APPLICATIONS OF MAGNESIUM ALLOYS

Magnesium castings are used in the aircraft industry for landing wheels, undercarriage legs, gas-turbine engine air intakes and engine support plates and frames. In the automobile industry crankcases and clutch and gear housings may be made from magnesium alloys. The Mg-Al-Zn alloys are used extensively for textile machinery, portable tools, vacuum cleaners, printing machinery and camera bodies. Magnesium is used for the manufacture of anodes for the cathodic protection of steel.

Magnesium alloys in the form of sheet, pressings and forgings are used for air frames and welded petrol and oil tanks and for parts of the fuselage and wings of many aircraft.

12. Miscellaneous Non-ferrous Metals and Alloys

NICKEL AND ITS ALLOYS

NICKEL

Commercially pure nickel contains approximately 99·5% nickel together with small amounts of Cu, Fe, Mn, Si, C and S. In general with more than 0·005% sulphur a brittle grain-boundary film of nickel sulphide is formed. This can be overcome by the presence of up to 0·2% magnesium to ensure the formation of magnesium sulphide instead of nickel sulphide.

Nickel possesses a good combination of strength and corrosion resistance. It has a particularly good resistance to corrosion by caustic alkalis, ammonia salt solutions and organic acids. It is strongly magnetic.

Typical mechanical properties of commercial nickel in the form of sheet and strip are as follows:

Condition	0·2% P.S.	U.T.S.	EL	V.P.N.
Cold-rolled (hard)	34–38	40–44	8–12	180–210
Cold-rolled + annealed	5–10	22–36	50–35	90–120

Nickel is used as anodes for nickel-plating, for chemical plant construction, and in the manufacture of food-handling equipment, due to its non-toxic properties.

NICKEL ALLOYS

A considerable number of nickel alloys are available for a wide range

109

of applications. Typical well-known alloys manufactured by Henry Wiggin Co. Ltd. are *Monel, Inconel*, the *Nimonic Series*, the *Bright Ray Series* and *Corronel*.

Monel

Monel contains approximately two-thirds of nickel and one-third of copper with smaller amounts of manganese, iron, silicon and carbon. It has a good resistance to corrosion to fresh and salt water, alkalis, reducing acids, alkaline solutions and super-heated steam. Its good mechanical properties are all maintained at elevated temperatures. Typical mechanical properties in the form of sheet or strip are as follows:

Condition	0·2% P.S.	U.T.S.	EL	V.P.N.
Hard-rolled	38–48	45–54	15–2	200 min.
Cold-rolled + annealed	11–20	31–38	50–30	100–140

Monel is used in both the cast and wrought conditions. It is used in power plant for such applications as valve seats and spindles, pump rods, pump spindles and impellers, corrugated joint rings, needles and nozzles in Pelton wheel installations and turbine blading. It is also used for pickling crates and for chemical and food-processing equipment.

K-Monel

The addition of 2–4% aluminium to Monel enables the alloy to be heat-treated so as to obtain improved mechanical properties, whilst retaining the corrosion resistance of Monel. This alloy known as K-Monel also possesses good elastic properties at low and high temperatures.

Solution treatment is carried out at 950°–1,000°C. The alloy is then precipitation-hardened at 590°C. for up to sixteen hours followed by controlled cooling. Precipitation-hardening may be carried out on the soft or cold-worked alloy. In the latter case the effect of work-hardening and temper-hardening may be combined. Typical mechanical properties of K-Monel in the cold-worked and thermally hardened condition are as follows:

0·2% P.S.	U.T.S.	EL	V.P.N.	Izod
44–58	62–75	30–15	280–340	26

K-Monel is used for propeller shafts, highly stressed nuts and bolts, pressure-sensitive instruments, e.g. pressure gauges, bellows and diaphragms.

Inconel

Inconel contains approximately 15% chromium, 8% iron, balance nickel. It combines good corrosion resistance with good mechanical properties and resistance to oxidation at elevated temperatures. At elevated temperatures a closely adherent oxide film is formed which retards further oxidation. Typical mechanical properties in the form of sheet and strip are as follows:

Condition	0·2% P.S.	U.T.S.	EL	V.P.N.
Hard-rolled	35–50	45–60	12–2	230–270
Cold-rolled + annealed	20–25	36–46	30–20	160–200

Inconel is used extensively for food-processing equipment and chemical plant. Due to its heat resistance it is used for aero-engine exhaust manifolds, thermocouple sheaths, protective sheathing for electric-heating elements, furnace components, enamelling racks and garter springs on steam turbines.

The Nimonic Series of Alloys

These alloys are basically nickel-chromium alloys which possess good creep, fatigue and oxidation resistance at elevated temperatures. The high creep strength of such alloys is obtained by the addition of such elements as titanium and aluminium which give rise to precipitation-hardening systems. The main use is in jet engines for flame tubes, rotor blades and discs.

Nimonic 75 is of the 80:20 Ni:Cr type, containing 0·2–0·6% Ti and up to 0·15% C. It is the standard material for gas-turbine flame tubes. Nimonic 80 and 80A are similar in basic composition but contain 0·5–1·8% aluminium in addition to 1·8–2·7% titanium and up to 0·1% carbon. Nimonic 80, introduced in 1941, was the first of these Nimonic alloys developed for gas-turbine blades and discs. Nimonic 80 and 80A are solution treated at 1,080°C. for eight hours, followed by air cooling and aged at 700°C. for sixteen hours, followed by air cooling. These alloys are suitable for use up to 750°C. Nimonic 90 and 95 contain 15–21% cobalt replacing nickel and may be used up to 870°C. and 940°C. respectively. Nimonic 100 is somewhat similar to Nimonic 90 in composition but contains 5% molybdenum, and is used for service temperatures up to 950°C. Nimonic 105 and the latest alloy Nimonic 115 show a further improvement in properties and operating temperature.

It is obvious that alloys which possess strength at high temperatures will present difficulties in hot-working. Many of these difficulties have been overcome by the development of glass lubrication for extrusion.

The Electrical-Resistance Alloys

These are based upon the 80:20 Ni:Cr composition and combine high electrical resistance and resistance to oxidation at elevated temperatures up to 1,150°–1,250°C. The Ni:Cr:Fe alloys containing approximately 20% iron are suitable for use up to 950°C. These alloys are known by various trade names such as the 'Bright Ray Series', 'Nichrome' and 'Pyromic'.

Corronel

Corronel 210 contains approximately 66% nickel, 28% molybdenum and 6% iron. The alloy is noted particularly for its resistance to hydrochloric, sulphuric and phosphoric acids.

BEARING METALS
REQUIREMENTS OF A BEARING ALLOY

Before an alloy can be used as a bearing metal it must satisfy a number of requirements. It should be sufficiently hard to resist wear and abrasion, tough to withstand shock loads, and strong enough to support the dead weight of the shaft. At the same time it should possess sufficient plasticity to allow of self-alignment. This combination of properties is, with certain exceptions, best achieved by using an alloy with a microstructure consisting of hard particles in a soft matrix. The hard particles provide the necessary wear resistance whilst the soft matrix allows local yielding. In service the soft matrix wears away below the level of the hard constituent. This not only reduces friction but also provides a series of minute oil grooves which aid lubrication.

In addition to the above properties a bearing alloy should possess good melting and casting properties and should bond readily to the backing or support. It is important that the alloy should have a low coefficient of friction to keep the bearing cool. The mechanical properties of the bearing should be maintained at slightly elevated temperatures. A resistance to corrosion by lubricants is also necessary.

A number of alloys are suitable for use as bearings and the choice will depend upon the load upon the bearing and the speed of rotation of the shaft. Bearing alloys may be classified according to composition as follows:

(1) COPPER-BASE BEARING ALLOYS
(2) WHITE-METAL BEARING ALLOYS
(3) CADMIUM-BASE BEARING ALLOYS

COPPER-BASE BEARING ALLOYS

The tin bronzes containing 10–15% tin and the cast phosphor-bronzes have already been discussed (Chapter 10). The hard constituent is provided by the $(\alpha + \delta)$ eutectoid in a soft matrix of the α solid solution. Other useful copper-base bearing alloys are the leaded bronzes containing 10–15% Pb or the straight copper-lead alloys containing 25–30% Pb. Lead is insoluble in copper and appears as globules in the microstructure. Lead improves plasticity and so allows for any lack of fit or alignment of bearings. The addition of 1–3% tin to the copper-lead bearing alloy assists casting by reducing the tendency to segregation of the lead globules. In general copper-base alloys are capable of carrying higher loads than the white metal bearings.

Porous-bronze bearings can be manufactured by powder metallurgy methods. Such bearings are manufactured by heating a compressed mixture of powdered copper, tin and graphite at about 700°–800°C. The porous-bronze bearing produced behaves like a solid sponge and soaks up considerable quantities of oil. During service this oil is fed to the bearing surface, being filtered as it passes through the metal. The presence of graphite also aids lubrication.

WHITE-METAL BEARING ALLOYS

The term 'white metal' covers both tin-base and lead-base bearing alloys.

TIN-BASE BEARING ALLOYS

The chief elements added to tin to provide the hard constituents are antimony and copper. These Sn-Sb-Cu alloys are frequently referred to as 'Babbitt metal' although the original 'Babbitt metal' was one specific alloy containing 89% tin, 7·4% antimony and 3·6% copper.

113

The tin-rich portion of the tin-antimony diagram is shown in Fig. 12.1.

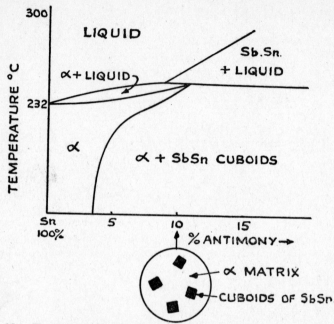

Fig. 12.1. The Tin-rich Portion of the Sn-Sb Equilibrium Diagram illustrating Microstructure of a 10% Sb Alloy

An alloy containing 10% antimony will consist of relatively hard cuboids of the compound SbSn in a soft matrix of the α solid solution. During the freezing of the alloy these cuboids, being lighter than the liquid, tend to float to the surface. The addition of copper gives rise to another hard constituent Cu_6Sn_5 which exists in the form of needle-shaped crystals. These crystals have a higher freezing point than SbSn and, during freezing, they form a network which prevents the SbSn cuboids floating to the surface. The

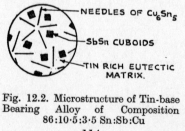

Fig. 12.2. Microstructure of Tin-base Bearing Alloy of Composition 86:10·5:3·5 Sn:Sb:Cu

114

microstructure of a typical tin-base bearing alloy is shown in Fig. 12.2.

For big-end bearings an alloy containing 93% tin, 3·5% antimony and 3·5% copper is used. This has a Brinell hardness of about 25. The alloy containing 86% tin, 10·5% antimony and 3·5% copper is suitable for main bearings and high-duty bearings for general purposes and has a Brinell Hardness of about 33.

Tin-base bearing alloys are superior in most respects to lead-base bearings, but the latter are cheaper.

LEAD-BASE BEARING ALLOYS

Lead-base bearing alloys are used for less severe service conditions. Antimony and tin are the chief hardening elements, although alkaline earth metals such as calcium and barium may also be used.

Lead and antimony form a eutectic containing 13% antimony which melts at 248°C. The microstructures of lead-base bearings will vary with composition. Magnolia metal (80Pb 15Sb 5Sn) consists of cuboids of practically pure antimony in a lead-rich eutectic matrix.

CADMIUM-BASE BEARING ALLOYS

Cadmium-base bearing alloys have superior mechanical properties to tin-base alloys, but are inferior to the latter in respect of corrosion resistance, plasticity and anti-frictional properties. Nickel, copper and silver may be present in amounts up to 2%. Hard microconstituents such as $NiCd_7$ and $CuCd_3$ may be formed, but silver usually goes into solid solution.

ZINC AND ITS ALLOYS

Zinc is mainly used as a protective coating for steel and may be applied by either galvanizing, sherardizing or spraying (Chapter 14).

Zinc-base alloys are being increasingly used in the form of gravity and pressure die castings. These zinc-base die castings are usually known under the trade name of 'Mazak' alloys and are covered by B.S. 1004. Typical composition properties are as follows:

Alloy	British Standard	Nominal composition			Original mechanical properties			
		Al	Cu	Mg	U.T.S.	EL	Impact*	B.H.N.
Mazak 3	1004 A	4·1	—	0·04	18·5	15·2	42·0	83
Mazak 5	1004 B	4·1	1·0	0·04	21·7	9·2	42·9	92

* Charpy Test. Unnotched specimen $\frac{1}{4}$ in. × $\frac{1}{4}$ in.

These alloys undergo a very slight shrinkage on ageing at room temperatures. This shrinkage can be brought almost to completion by a stabilizing treatment at 100°C. for six hours, without any appreciable effect on the mechanical properties. Mazak 3 is used where the highest dimensional stability is required and where castings are likely to be subject to heat in service. This alloy is preferred for general-purpose die casting. Mazak 5 is used where maximum castability in production is desired or where a harder and stronger alloy is required.

Very small amounts of tin, cadmium and lead are detrimental since they cause intercrystalline corrosion, causing an increase in dimensions and in some cases excessive swelling and cracking. This has now been overcome by the use of high purity 99·99% zinc.

LEAD AND ITS ALLOYS

Lead was one of the earliest metals known to man. It is mentioned in the Old Testament where it was used for ornamental objects and structural purposes. Lead mines were worked in Britain as early as the first century A.D. It was in general use for water pipes in Roman times.

Lead is characterized by high resistance to corrosion, low melting point (327°C.), high specific gravity (11·3), and good malleability. It is the softest of metals in common use and can be extruded as pipe or rolled into thin sheets. Lead is used for electric cable sheathing, water pipes, roofing sheets, and in the chemical industry for the storage and transport of corrosive liquids.

Lead-base alloys hardened by antimony and tin are used for bearing metals (page 115) whilst lead-tin alloys are used for soft soldering (page 118). Lead-antimony alloys containing 7–12% antimony are used for storage-battery grids.

TYPE METALS

The ternary alloys of lead, tin and antimony are used for the founding of type for printing purposes. Lead-base alloys used for slug-casting machines such as the Linotype and Intertype machines contain 10–13% antimony and 2–4% tin. Other examples are Monotype alloy (7–10% Sn 14–19% Sb) and stereotype alloy (3–10% Sn 14–17% Sb). These alloys are characterized by low melting point, high fluidity, good wear resistance and absence of solidification shrinkage.

FUSIBLE ALLOYS

Fusible alloys are low-melting-point alloys containing bismuth, lead and tin as the chief ingredients. Other metals such as cadmium, antimony, and mercury may also be present. These alloys are usually of eutectic or near-eutectic composition and are used for metal patterns, die mounting, fillers for tube bending, constant-temperature baths for the heat treatment of steel, safety plugs in boilers, and fire sprinklers. The mercury-containing alloys are used in dental work. Some typical fusible alloys are given in the table below:

Name	Composition per cent.					Melting range °C.
	Bi	Pb	Sn	Cd	Sb	
'Cerrobend'	50	26·7	13·3	10	—	70–73
'Cerromatrix'	48	28·5	14·5	—	9	103–227
Wood's Metal	50	25·0	12·5	12·5	—	70–72
Rose's Alloy	50	28·0	22·0	—	—	96–110

13. The Joining of Metals and Alloys

The chief methods used for the joining of metals may be classified as follows:

1. SOFT SOLDERING
2. BRAZING
3. WELDING

SOFT SOLDERING

In soft soldering, as in brazing, a thin film of molten alloy is introduced between the parts to be joined at a temperature below the melting point of those parts. The soft solder employed must fulfil the following requirements:

(a) Its melting point must be lower than that of the metals to be joined, but higher than the expected service temperature.

(b) It must 'wet' and flow freely over the surfaces of the metal to be joined.

(c) It should solidify as a sound film of metal and adhere firmly to the work.

(d) It must have adequate mechanical strength. For most soft solders the strength of the joint is about 3–4 tons per sq. in.

The soft solders commercially employed are either tin-lead alloys or 'antimonial' tin-lead alloys containing up to 3% antimony. These alloys are covered by B.S. 219, 1959. Antimonial solders are slightly cheaper since antimony replaces expensive tin. They are suitable for most purposes but should not be used for soldering galvanized iron components since they form weak alloys with zinc.

The two main soft soldering alloys are tinman's solder (62% Sn 38% Pb) and plumber's solder (67% Pb 33% Sn) (Fig. 13.1). Tinman's solder is of eutectic composition and is therefore the

118

lowest-melting-point alloy in the series. It is used for electrical, radio and instrument assemblies and machine soldering of can-end seams. Plumber's solder freezes over a range of temperature and thus has a pasty stage which enables the joint to be 'wiped'. Plumber's solder is used in the wiping of lead cable and pipe joints.

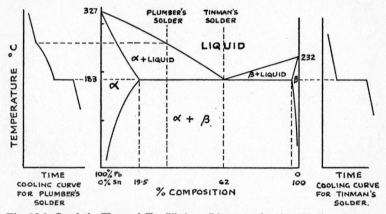

Fig. 13.1. Lead-tin Thermal Equilibrium Diagram showing Cooling Curves for Tinman's and Plumber's Solder

A flux is essential in soft soldering to remove oxide films and expose clean surfaces over which the molten solder can flow. The flux also prevents oxidation of the solder. Typical fluxes are zinc chloride ('killed spirits') and ammonium chloride ('sal ammoniac') or mixtures of both. These fluxes are corrosive and should be re-moved by washing after soldering. Rosin-cored solder wire (B.S. 441, 1954) is widely used in this country, particularly for electrical purposes. These contain wood or gum rosin with or without an 'activator' which acts as a non-corrosive flux.

BRAZING

From the metallurgical point of view brazing is similar to soft soldering except that a higher-melting-point alloy is used for making the joint. Brazing alloys are stronger and are capable of withstand-ing higher service temperatures.

Brazing alloys may be classified into three main types as specified in B.S. 1845, 1952.

(1) Silver-bearing brazing alloys or 'silver solders'
(2) Phosphorus-bearing brazing alloys
(3) Brazing brasses.

(1) SILVER-BEARING BRAZING ALLOYS

Brazing using these alloys is usually referred to as silver soldering. Silver solders are essentially Ag-Cu-Zn alloys with or without cadmium, which have a lower melting point than the usual brazing brasses. The composition and approximate freezing ranges of these alloys are shown in Table 13.1.

B.S. 1845 Type	Ag	Cu	Zn	Cd	Approx. Freezing Range °C.
3	49–51	14–16	15–17	18–20	620–640
4	60–62	27·5–29·5	9–11	—	690–735
5	42–44	36–38	18·5–20·5	—	700–775

Table 13.1. Compositions of Typical Silver Solders

The first of the alloys (Type 3) is known commercially as *Easy-Flo*. It has a small freezing range and its composition approaches that of the Ag-Cu-Zn-Cd eutectic. Silver solders are very free-flowing and strong joints (22–29 t.s.i.) can be made with very little heat-effect on the parent metal.

The choice of flux in silver soldering and brazing generally depends upon the temperature. In general for brazing alloys melting above 760°C. a borax-type flux is used. Below this temperature a fluoride-type flux is employed since those of the borax type are too viscous at these temperatures.

(2) PHOSPHORUS-BEARING BRAZING ALLOYS

The phosphorus-containing brazing alloys are usually referred to as self-fluxing brazing alloys. When melted in air the products of oxidation form a fluid compound which acts as an effective flux. These alloys are only effective if melted in an oxidizing atmosphere. They should not be applied to ferrous or nickel-base alloys since they form brittle compounds which weaken the joint. Typical compositions are shown below.

These alloys are known commercially under various trade names, e.g. *Cupro-Tectic* and *Silbralloy* (Cu-P), and *Silfos* (80:15:5 Cu-Ag-P).

B.S. 1845 Type	Ag	P	Cu	Freezing range °C.
6	13–15	4–6	Balance	625–780
7	—	7·0–7·5	Balance	705–800

(3) BRAZING BRASSES

The oldest and best-known method of brazing involves the use of brazing brasses or 'brazing spelter', using borax as a flux. Typical compositions of brazing brasses are shown in Table 13.2. These alloys melt at higher temperatures than the silver solders but sound

B.S. 1845 Type	Cu	Zn	Sn	Approx. freezing range °C.
8	49–51	Balance	—	860–870
9	53–55	,,	—	870–880
10	59–61	,,	—	885–890
11	53–55	,,	0·8–1·2	860–870
12	59–61	,,	0·8–1·2	880–890

Table 13.2. Brazing Brasses

joints having tensile strengths of 25–30 tons per sq. in. are possible. Bonding in brazing is due to mutual alloying of the base metal and the brazing alloy.

BRAZING OF ALUMINIUM

For aluminium brazing special filler alloys of the aluminium-silicon type are used. These are covered by B.S. 1942, 1953.

WELDING

Welding processes may be broadly classified into two types, viz.
1. Fusion-welding processes
2. Pressure-welding processes
The distinction between these types is summarized in Table 13.3.

Fusion-welding processes	*Pressure-welding processes*
1. Metals to be joined are locally melted.	1. Metals to be joined do not melt.*
2. No pressure applied.	2. Pressure applied to form the joint.
3. Extra metal added in the form of a filler wire or consumable electrode.	3. No additional metal required.

Table 13.3. Distinction Between Fusion and Pressure-welding Processes
*In electrical resistance welding some melting takes place.

The various welding processes employed will not be discussed in this book but a classification of the chief processes is shown below:

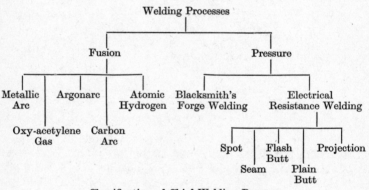

Classification of Chief Welding Processes

METALLURGICAL ASPECTS OF WELDING

The metallurgical aspects of welding are particularly interesting since in a welded joint we have examples of cast, wrought, and heat-treated structures. The weld deposit will possess a typical cast structure with all its inherent defects. The heat-affected zone of the parent metal will exhibit the effects of heat-treatment, whilst the unaffected portion will probably reveal a typical wrought structure. Welded joints may therefore be studied under the following headings.

1. The weld metal deposit
2. The heat-affected zone of the parent metal

1. THE WELD METAL

The weld metal is, in effect, a miniature casting which has cooled rapidly from an extremely high temperature. Long columnar crystals may therefore be formed giving rise to a relatively weak structure (Fig. 13.2 (a)). In a multi-run weld each deposit 'normal-

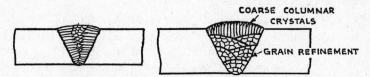

(a) Single-run Weld   (b) Multi-run Weld
Fig. 13.2. Diagrammatic Representation of Structure of Weld Metal in Single and Multi-run Weld Deposit

izes' the preceding run and considerable grain refinement is obtained with consequent improvement in mechanical properties. In this case only the top run exhibits a coarse 'cast' structure and this can largely be removed after welding if necessary.

The effect of the correct welding temperature on the structure of a spot weld is shown in Fig. 13.3.

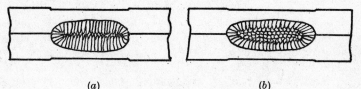

(a)   (b)
Fig. 13.3. Structure of Spot Welds

If the welding temperature is too high the columnar crystals will meet at the centre, forming a plane of weakness (Fig. 13.3 (a)) which may lead to intercrystalline cracking. If the temperature is correct then equi-axed grains will form at the centre before the columnar crystals can meet (Fig. 13.3 (b)). The importance of correct control of current and time in spot welding is therefore apparent.

Other possible defects in the weld metal include non-metallic inclusions, gas porosity, and cracking.

NON-METALLIC INCLUSIONS

The formation of oxide and nitride inclusions due to atmospheric contamination is usually avoided by the use of a flux. Modern flux-coated electrodes usually provide good quality weld deposits substantially free from harmful inclusions. In the argon-arc welding process, the metal is deposited under a shroud of the inert gas argon, which prevents oxidation, and no flux is necessary. Slag inclusions can be avoided in multi-run welds by effective removal of the slag after each deposit.

GAS POROSITY

The chief cause of gas porosity is the presence of hydrogen in the weld metal, or the reaction of hydrogen with any oxide present in the melted parent metal to form steam. The solubility of hydrogen in most metals such as copper, aluminium and iron varies with temperature as shown in Fig. 13.4.

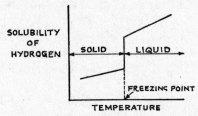

SOLUBILITY OF HYDROGEN

SOLID

LIQUID

FREEZING POINT

TEMPERATURE

Fig. 13.4. Solubility of Hydrogen in Weld Metal

Hydrogen is readily soluble in the liquid state but only slightly soluble in the solid state. Considerable quantities of hydrogen are therefore evolved upon solidification which may cause gas porosity in the solid weld metal.

In the welding of tough-pitch copper, which contains a small amount of oxygen in the form of cuprous oxide, the hydrogen may react with the oxide of the melted parent metal to form steam. The steam produced by this reaction may give rise to unsoundness.

There are numerous sources of hydrogen in welding, the chief ones being the welding flame in gas welding or the flux coating in metallic arc welding.

WELD-METAL CRACKING

Welded joints which are prepared under restraint are liable to intercrystalline cracking in the weld deposit due to contractional strains set up during the cooling of the metal. Such cracking, usually known as 'hot cracking', is largely related to the grain size and the presence of grain boundary impurities. At high temperatures the grain boundaries are more able to accommodate shrinkage strains than the grains themselves. A coarse-grained deposit, with large

124

columnar crystals, possesses a relatively small grain boundary area and is therefore more susceptible to hot cracking. The presence of low-melting-point grain boundary films, e.g. ferrous sulphide in mild steel deposits, is also known to give rise to hot cracking. The addition of the correct proportion of manganese results in the formation of manganese sulphide which has a higher melting point and the susceptibility to cracking is thus greatly reduced.

Fundamental work carried out on the welding of aluminium alloys* has shown that weld-metal cracking can be divided into that which occurs above the solidus and that which occurs below the solidus. It was found that cracking of the former type occurred mainly in alloys which solidified over a range of temperature. Pure metals and eutectic alloys were not susceptible to cracking at high temperatures. Sub-solidus cracking is not as frequent as that which occurs above the solidus.

2. THE HEAT-AFFECTED ZONE OF THE PARENT METAL

It is not easy to generalize when considering the effect of welding heat on the structure and properties of the parent metal. The extent of any structural change will depend upon the time at temperature, and consequently such factors as the thermal conductivity, specific heat, and dimensions of the plate, together with the speed and method of welding are important. Welded joints prepared from metals of high thermal conductivity, such as copper and aluminium, possess wider heat-affected zones than those prepared from nickel or steel. Metallic-arc welding produces a more concentrated heating effect than gas welding. Increase in the welding speed also reduces the width of the heat-affected zone.

In general with non-ferrous metals and alloys it would be expected that softening of work-hardened or age-hardened metal would occur in the heat-affected zone. The softening effect in age-hardened alloys is usually more sluggish but is a problem in the welding of heat-treated aluminium alloys. In addition grain growth usually occurs in non-ferrous alloys but this is usually insufficient to have any great effect on the strength of the welded joint. The structure of the heat-affected zone of a typical weld preparation in hard-rolled aluminium sheet is shown in Fig. 13.5.

The heat-affected zone in mild steel plate will exhibit various structures, ranging from an overheated structure (Fig. 5.3(a)) for those parts heated to well above the upper critical range to an underannealed structure (Fig. 5.3(b)) for those parts heated to within

*Aluminium Development Association. Research Report No. 2.

the critical range. The welding of mild steel presents no serious difficulties.

In contrast to most non-ferrous alloys an increase in hardness will occur in the heat affected zones of steels. The degree of hardening increases with increasing tensile strength of the steel.

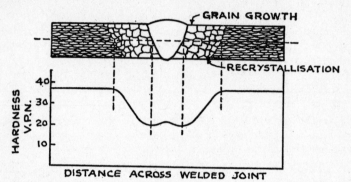

Fig. 13.5. Effect of Welding on the Structure and Hardness of Hard-rolled Aluminium Sheet

HARD-ZONE CRACKING

With certain low-alloy high-tensile steels a hard martensitic structure may form in the heat-affected zone of plate. When the joint is prepared under restraint there is a tendency to cracking in this

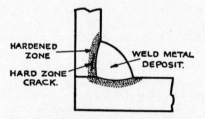

Fig. 13.6. Hard-zone Crack in a Welded Joint in Low-Alloy Steel

hardened zone. The hardness of the heat-affected zone will depend upon the composition of the steel and the rate of cooling. Preheating to about 200°C., the use of large-gauge electrodes, and slow welding speeds, are all effective in reducing hardness and cracking tendency. It has also been found that cracking can be overcome by the use of either low-hydrogen electrodes or fully austenitic electrodes.

The effectiveness of low-hydrogen electrodes suggests that the presence of hydrogen is a factor in hard-zone cracking. Hydrogen is soluble in austenite but insoluble in martensite and ferrite. Hydrogen from the weld deposit diffuses into the heat-affected zone which, during welding, is in the austenitic condition. When transformation to martensite takes place the hydrogen is rejected, collects in micro-fissures, and builds up a pressure which eventually leads to cracking. The use of austenitic weld metal minimizes diffusion of hydrogen since it retains most of the hydrogen in the weld deposit. It is advisable to combine austenitic electrodes with low-hydrogen coatings.

FORTIWELD STEEL

Because of the danger of hard-zone cracking most of the commercial low-alloy high-tensile steels can only be welded using special procedures. The best combination of mechanical properties and weldability is possessed by a steel known as *Fortiweld*. This steel developed by Appleby-Frodingham Steel Co. Ltd. was first reported in a paper by Bardgett and Reeve in 1949. Fortiweld is a low-carbon molybdenum-boron steel of the following approximate analysis:

C	Mn	Mo	B
0·10–0·16	0·5	0·5	0·0015–0·0035

Fortiweld possesses a yield point of 30 t.s.i. and an U.T.S. of 40 t.s.i. in the 'as rolled' condition. The good mechanical properties are combined with a weldability almost equivalent to that of mild steel.

WELDING OF CAST IRONS

The welding of cast iron usually involves the repair of fractured castings. Considerable experience is therefore necessary since each repair job usually requires a somewhat different technique.

Cast iron has a low ductility and further cracking is likely to occur due to the stresses set up by the rapid localized heating and cooling. Hard brittle weld deposits may be formed due to absorption of carbon from the molten parent metal. If the cooling rate is rapid the heat affected zone of the parent metal will also be hardened due to the formation of martensite. These defects can be overcome to a large extent by preheating to about 500°–600°C. followed by slow cooling, either in a furnace or under a blanket of sand. In gas welding, the use of a filler wire containing a high silicon content reduces the tendency to form hard white-iron deposits. In metallic-arc welding, if preheating is not possible, a special electrode giving a nickel alloy deposit can be employed. This avoids the formation of a hard deposit since nickel does not form hard compounds with carbon from the parent metal.

WELDING OF AUSTENITIC STAINLESS STEELS

The problem of carbide precipitation in the heat affected zone of the parent metal during the welding of austenitic stainless steels has already been discussed (page 70). A neutral flame should be employed in oxy-acetylene gas welding, and since a slightly carburizing flame could lead to carbon pick-up, this process is only recommended where maximum corrosion resistance is not required. In metallic-arc welding a niobium-stabilized electrode should be employed even if the parent metal has been stabilized with titanium. This is due to the loss of titanium that occurs during the transfer of molten metal across the arc. Argon-arc welding is being increasingly employed since it avoids the use of corrosive fluxes.

WELDING OF ALUMINIUM AND ITS ALLOYS

The chief processes employed are the oxy-acetylene gas and argon-arc welding processes. Spot welding is extensively used in the aircraft industry. Among the factors to be considered in the welding of aluminium are the relatively low melting point, high thermal capacity and conductivity, high coefficient of expansion and rapid oxidation of the metal. The use of a flux is essential in gas welding to remove the oxide film, and since flux residues are corrosive they should be removed thoroughly after welding. In gas welding, a strictly neutral flame should be employed. Gas porosity due to hydrogen and tendency to cracking have been discussed previously.

WELDING OF COPPER AND ITS ALLOYS

Difficulties are encountered in the welding of tough-pitch copper. In the wrought condition, this grade of copper contains oxygen in the form of dispersed particles of cuprous oxide which are not detrimental to the mechanical properties. However, when the copper is remelted, the oxide dissolves, and upon solidification it forms a eutectic at the grain boundaries. This type of structure would be present in the weld metal and in those parts of the parent metal which have been heated to above the solidus temperature. Intermittent welding is employed for tough-pitch copper, with hammering of the hot welds to break up and disperse the oxide. Tough-pitch copper also gives rise to gas porosity in the weld metal due to gas-metal reactions (page 124), and to 'gassing' in the heat-affected zone of the parent metal (page 87). Where possible, deoxidized copper is employed for welding, and the use of a deoxidizer filler wire containing 0·05% P and 1·0% Ag is common practice for all grades of copper. The thermal conductivity of copper is about eight times that of mild steel and preheating is essential in order to obtain fusion.

The chief problem in the welding of brass is the volatilization of zinc. Zinc boils at 906°C. and consequently vaporizes during welding, giving rise to porosity. The vapour oxidizes to form a white cloud of zinc oxide, which not only obstructs the vision of the welder, but is also poisonous.

Difficulties are encountered in the welding of aluminium-bronzes due to the formation of the tenacious film of aluminium oxide. However, satisfactory arc welding of these alloys has been made possible by the development of suitable electrodes.

WELDING OF NICKEL AND ITS ALLOYS

The physical properties of nickel such as melting point, thermal capacity, conductivity and thermal expansion and contraction are very similar to those of steel. Welding of nickel alloys presents few difficulties provided the weld is prepared without undue restraint. Nickel is particularly sensitive to sulphur attack (page 109) and thorough cleaning of the surface prior to welding is important.

14. The Corrosion of Metals

Because of its costly destructive effect the study of corrosion, and its prevention, is of vital importance to both the metallurgist and the engineer. Corrosion is a complex problem due to the many variables involved. The factors governing the rate of corrosion may be broadly divided into those relating to (1) the metal and (2) the environment.

The factors relating to the metal or alloy include (a) the position of the metal in the electro-chemical series; (b) contact with dissimilar metals; (c) microstructure, e.g. the presence of impurities or of a second constituent; and (d) the presence of internal stress. The factors involved when considering the effect of environment include (a) relative humidity; (b) presence of impurities in the atmosphere; (c) rate of supply and distribution of oxygen; (d) rate of flow of liquid; (e) the acidity or alkalinity of the liquid; and (f) presence of external stress. These are only a few of the factors involved but are sufficient to emphasize the complex nature of the problem.

In general two principal forms of corrosion can be distinguished:

1. Direct chemical corrosion
2. Electro-chemical corrosion

1. DIRECT CHEMICAL CORROSION

This type of corrosion usually involves direct combination between the metal and dry gases such as oxygen, sulphur dioxide, and chlorine, and usually occurs at high temperatures. The nature of the film produced has an important effect on the extent of subsequent corrosion. If the film is hard, adherent and protective, then corrosion will eventually cease, as in the case of the corrosion and heat-resisting alloys of the nickel-chromium type.

2. ELECTRO-CHEMICAL CORROSION

This type of corrosion covers all forms of "wet" corrosion, i.e. where the metal is in contact with a liquid or even a moist atmosphere. In the electro-chemical theory it is assumed that all metals have a tendency to dissolve or corrode, when the metal discharges positively-charged particles, called ions, into solution. This leaves the metal with a characteristic negative charge or potential. The greater the negative potential the greater is the tendency of the metal to dissolve or corrode. The corrosion resistance of metals is governed by their position in the electro-chemical series in which metals are arranged according to their electrode potentials (Table 14.1). The value of these potentials is very small and their results are expressed relative to hydrogen which is taken as zero.

Anodic end (corroded)	
Metal	Electrode potential volts
Sodium	−2·71
Magnesium	−2·40
Aluminium	−1·70
Zinc	−0·76
Chromium	−0·56
Iron	−0·44
Cadmium	−0·40
Nickel	−0·23
Tin	−0·14
Lead	−0·12
Hydrogen	0·00
Copper	+0·35
Silver	+0·80
Platinum	+1·20
Gold	+1·50
Cathodic End (protected)	

Table 14.1. The Electro-Chemical Series of Metals

The tendency of each individual metal to corrode is relatively small, but is greatly increased when it is in contact with a dissimilar metal in the presence of a conducting liquid, referred to as the electrolyte. A current will flow between the two metals since they

131

are at different potentials. Corrosion of the one higher in the table (known as the ANODE) will be accelerated whilst the metal lower in the table (known as the CATHODE) will be protected. The rate of corrosion is governed by the relative areas of the anode and the cathode. In general for a given area of anode, the attack increases in severity the greater the area of the adjacent cathode.

It will be seen that for electro-chemical corrosion to occur there must be a cathode, an anode and an electrolyte. The formation of an anode and cathode need not necessarily be due to contact with a dissimilar metal. Electrolytic corrosion can also occur due to the presence of an impurity or second constituent in the structure of the alloy, or to a local difference in oxygen concentration on the surface (differential aeration effect).

RELATIONSHIP BETWEEN MICROSTRUCTURE AND CORROSION-RESISTANCE

For maximum corrosion-resistance an alloy should be of the single solid-solution type. The presence of a second constituent or impurity can reduce the corrosion resistance due to electrolytic action. 'Weld decay' in austenitic stainless steels (page 70) is an example of the decrease in corrosion-resistance due to the precipitation of chromium-rich carbides from the solid-solution austenite. The corrosion resistance of some commercially pure metals such as magnesium can be greatly increased by decreasing the amount of impurities such as iron. When present in amounts greater than 0·003% the iron is present as a second constituent and this gives rise to electrolytic corrosion.

DIFFERENTIAL AERATION EFFECT

The work of Dr. U. R. Evans of Cambridge has shown that corrosion can take place even in a pure metal if there is a difference in oxygen concentration on the metal surface. This can be demonstrated using the apparatus shown in Fig. 14.1. If two pieces of the same metal are immersed in an electrolyte, no current is detected since there is no difference in potential between them. When one piece of metal is aerated a current is detected, the aerated metal being protected (cathode) whilst the non-aerated metal corrodes (anode). When the current of oxygen is diverted to the other compartment the direction of the current is reversed. This theory can be used to explain corrosion problems such as 'pitting', and also why metals corrode under scale deposits or along cracks and scratches more readily than elsewhere on the surface. A differential aeration cell could be set up when metal sheets are stacked together with water trapped between them. This could be due to differences in oxygen content among the pockets of liquid held between the sheets by surface tension.

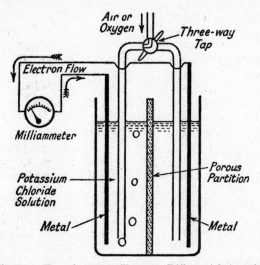

Fig. 14.1. Experiment to illustrate Differential Aeration Effect. From *Introduction to Metallic Corrosion* by U. R. Evans (Edward Arnold)

PITTING

Pitting is an example of the differential aeration effect. The initial depression or pit in the surface may be the result of several factors, e.g. a break in a protective film or scale, or the solution of a non-metallic inclusion due to electrolytic action. Once a pit is formed the corrosion proceeds rapidly since the surface of the metal (cathode) has a greater access to oxygen than the base of the pit (anode) (Fig. 14.2). Corrosion is accelerated by the fact that the surface area of the cathode is considerably greater than that of the anode.

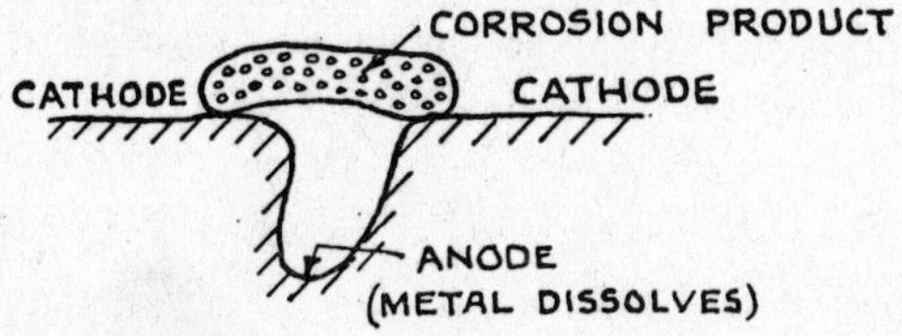

Fig. 14.2. 'Pitting' Corrosion

The corrosion product accumulates at the mouth of the pit and assists corrosion by making oxygen diffusion more difficult.

STRESS CORROSION

This is due to the simultaneous action of sustained static stress and corrosion and is mainly associated with the alloys of magnesium and aluminium, brasses and stainless steels. The stresses involved are usually internal stresses induced by some previous treatment such as cold-working. The corrosive attack is along the grain boundaries, thereby considerably weakening the alloy. One of the earliest and best-known examples is that of the 'season-cracking' of brass cartridge cases. Season-cracking is the name given to the intercrystalline cracking that occurs when work-hardened brasses are exposed to mildly corrosive media, e.g. industrial atmospheres. It is caused by the relief of internal stress and can be overcome by annealing at 280°–300°C. This will relieve the internal stresses without softening the alloy. The 'caustic embrittlement' of riveted steel boilers is another example. This is attributed to the combined effect of caustic soda and high local stress of the boiler metal, e.g. at rivet holes. The caustic soda is formed from 'soda ash' added to the boiler feed water.

PASSIVITY

Certain alloys, particularly stainless steels, are capable of forming a thin protective oxide film when used in contact with an oxidizing medium such as nitric acid. The alloy is said to become 'passive' since corrosion is greatly minimized. This film does not offer such good protection against corrosion by less oxidizing acids such as hydrochloric or sulphuric acid.

EFFECT OF DESIGN ON CORROSION

The importance of correct design cannot be over-emphasized. Contact with the corrosive medium should be reduced to a minimum. Adequate drainage and ventilation should be provided, and the design should aim to prevent crevices or moisture traps. Attention should be paid to sealing of joints since if aqueous liquid cannot intrude there can be no corrosion. In this connection butt welded joints are generally better than riveted joints.

PROTECTION OF METALS AND ALLOYS FROM CORROSION

Certain alloys possess an inherent resistance to various types of corrosion, e.g. stainless steel, nickel, Monel and Inconel. However, these alloys are expensive and their use cannot be economically justified except for special applications such as chemical plant construction. It is therefore necessary to adopt various methods to protect metals and alloys from corrosion. The methods used may be broadly classified as follows:

1. *METALLIC COATINGS*
These coatings may be applied by (*a*) dipping, (*b*) electro-deposition, (*c*) cladding, (*d*) spraying, (*e*) cementation methods such as calorizing, sherardizing and chromizing.

2. *NON-METALLIC COATINGS*
These include oxide and phosphate films and protection by various paints, varnishes and lacquers.

3. *CATHODIC PROTECTION*
The metal is sacrificially protected by contact with another metal which is higher in the electro-chemical series.

Each of these methods of protection will now be discussed in more detail.

1. PROTECTION BY METALLIC COATINGS

(*a*) *Hot Dipping*
This method is used in the manufacture of tin plate and of galvanized-iron sheet. The thoroughly cleaned steel is passed through a layer of molten flux into a bath of molten tin or zinc. A thin layer of tin or zinc adheres to the steel due to the formation of a thin zone of an iron-tin or iron-zinc alloy. The process of tin-plating by dipping has to a large extent been replaced by electrolytic tinning. Tin-plate with a coating of the order of 0·00005 in. thick is used extensively in the canning industry.

Zinc is anodic to steel and therefore if the coating is broken the zinc will corrode sacrificially. This is an example of the sacrificial protection of steel. On the other hand tin is cathodic to steel and the protection is purely mechanical. The tin coating must be of good quality since if it is ruptured then corrosion of the steel will be accelerated by electrolytic action.

(*b*) *Electro-deposition or Electro-plating*
The component to be plated is made the cathode in an electrolytic cell. The plating solution, or electrolyte, consists usually of a salt of

the plating metal together with various special additions. The anode consists of the plating metal, which, when the current is passed, dissolves and plates out on the cathode. In some cases, as in chromium plating, an insoluble anode may be used, when the chromium is provided by the electrolyte itself.

The usual thickness of deposits of the commonly plated metals are nickel (0·0003 in.–0·0020 in.), chromium (0·00001 in.–0·00005 in.), copper (0·0003 in.–0·0010 in.), cadmium (0·0002 in.–0·0005 in.) and silver (0·0003 in.–0·0012 in.)

No alloying is involved and adhesion depends entirely upon the intimate contact of the coating and base metal. The components for plating must therefore be thoroughly cleaned.

(c) Cladding

The use of clad steels was developed for the chemical industry in order to avoid the expense of using thicker plates of corrosion-resistant materials such as nickel, Monel, and stainless steel. Clad steels are manufactured by hot-rolling composite billets, to produce a cladding thickness equal to 5–20% of the total thickness of the plate. Superficial alloying takes place at the interface.

Aluminium alloys are frequently protected from corrosion by a cladding of pure aluminium, applied by hot-rolling. The usual clad thickness is about 10% of the total thickness.

(d) Spraying

Metallic coatings of aluminium, zinc, tin, copper, lead, brass and bronze may be applied by spraying. The molten metal is sprayed from a pistol in which the metal in wire form is melted by an electric arc or oxy-acetylene flame and blown out by compressed air. The adherence of sprayed coatings to the base metal is lower than the other methods previously mentioned. No alloying occurs and the surface should be clean and preferably roughened. The usual thickness of zinc and aluminium coatings is 0·004 in.–0·012 in.

(e) Cementation Processes

Examples of cementation processes are sherardizing, calorizing and chromizing. In each case the component is surrounded by powdered metal and heated when alloying of the two metals occurs.

Sherardizing. A uniform coating of zinc is obtained by heating the compound in zinc dust at 350°–373°C. for three to twelve hours. After three hours a film thickness of approximately 0·0025 in. is obtained.

Calorizing. A layer of an iron-aluminium alloy approximately 0·025–0·030 in. in thickness is obtained by heating mild steel in

136

powdered aluminium at 850°–1,000°C. Calorized steel has a good resistance to oxidation at elevated temperatures.

Chromizing. A chromium-rich surface is obtained by heating the steel in a powdered mixture of aluminium oxide and chromium in an atmosphere of hydrogen at 1,300°–1,400°C. for three to four hours. The hydrogen is necessary to prevent oxidation of the chromium.

2. NON-METALLIC COATINGS

Anodizing of Aluminium Alloys

Aluminium possesses a good resistance to corrosion due to the formation of a hard self-healing adherent oxide film on the surface. The object of anodizing is to increase the thickness of this film. This is achieved by making the component the anode in an electrolyte of either chromic, sulphuric or oxalic acid. The cathode consists of either stainless steel or lead. The oxide film varies in thickness according to the process used, but is normally 0·00001–0·00020 in. thick. The sulphuric acid process produces a thicker film and takes about 20–40 minutes. The chromic acid process produces a thinner, harder film and takes about one hour.

The anodized skin can be coloured by immersion in a solution containing a suitable dye. Sealing of the anodized skin is essential after anodizing in order to improve the corrosion-resistance and hardness. This can be achieved by immersion in boiling water for about 20 minutes or by the application of lanolin.

Hard anodic films approximately 0·002 in. in thickness are used for wear resistance. In order to build up such thick films a low temperature is necessary to keep the resistance of the bath low. This is usually achieved by refrigeration.

Chromating

Oxide films can be produced on magnesium alloys by dipping in solutions of potassium dichromate together with other additions. Chromate surfaces vary in colour but are usually grey or black. The treatment is generally followed by painting with a zinc chromate paint.

Phosphating

Phosphating treatments, such as *Parkerizing, Bonderizing, Granodizing* and *Walterizing* are usually carried out on steels and zinc-base alloys. A coating of phosphate is produced by immersion in a solution of acid iron, manganese, or zinc phosphates together with various accelerators. The time of immersion varies from 1–10 minutes. The surface produced is treated with varnish, paint or lacquer to improve the corrosion resistance. Phosphating treatment is carried out on motor car, cycle and refrigerator parts prior to enamelling.

3. CATHODIC PROTECTION

Metals such as magnesium are frequently employed as galvanic anodes for the protection of steel. Magnesium is higher than iron in the electro-chemical series and corrodes sacrificially. Cathodic protection is given to pipe lines, buried structures, and the hulls and compartments of ships.

15. The Examination and Non-destructive Testing of Metals and Alloys

One of the functions of a metallurgist attached to an engineering works is the examination of defects and service failures in metal components. In addition he is required to carry out various routine tests on both the incoming material and the manufactured product. It is therefore important that the engineering student should have some knowledge of the various methods of examination and testing, particularly their scope of application and limitations. The various methods of mechanical testing are not included in this book as it is assumed that this will be covered by the student in the subject of 'Strength of Materials'.

THE EXAMINATION OF FRACTURES

Valuable information regarding the cause of failure can often be obtained by a visual examination of the fracture. The presence of slag inclusions, porosity and blow holes is readily observed in the fractures of welded joints and castings. Fractures occurring during the hot-working of ingots are frequently the result of coarse columnar crystals forming planes of weakness (Fig. 1.8) due to the casting temperature being too high. Components subjected to alternating or reversed stresses are liable to fatigue failure. A fatigue fracture is usually characterized by two well-defined zones as shown in Fig. 15.1. The smooth discoloured portion is evidence of the gradual extension across the section of a crack, which frequently starts from some point of stress-concentration, e.g. a sharp fillet, tool mark, oil hole or slag inclusion. Once a crack has been initiated the applied load becomes more concentrated, causing gradual extension of the fracture. Finally the remaining area cannot sustain the load, and

139

breaks suddenly, giving a fibrous fracture. The difference between these two zones is not so apparent in the more brittle materials.

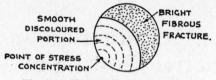

Fig. 15.1. Typical Fatigue Fracture

MACRO-EXAMINATION

Macro-examination involves the examination of prepared sections either with the naked eye or using a small hand magnifying lens. The surface to be examined need only be ground to about 0 or 00 emery paper and washed to remove the grit, before being deeply etched, using the appropriate etching reagents.

This method is useful in revealing flow lines in forgings (Fig. 2.8), grain size in castings, the contour of weld deposits and heat-affected zones in welded joints. Gross defects such as slag, porosity and blow holes in welds and castings are also readily visible without resorting to microscopical examination.

MACRO-ETCHING REAGENTS
STEEL

(1) *50% Hydrochloric Acid*

The specimen should be immersed in the boiling reagent for 10–45 minutes. In general the higher the carbon content the longer the etching times required. The reagent is used to reveal flow lines, the structure of welds, cracks and porosity.

(2) *25% Nitric Acid*

This reagent is similar to (1) but is used cold for large surfaces which cannot be conveniently heated.

(3) *10% Ammonium Persulphate Solution*

This reagent should be made up fresh and applied as a cold swab with absorbent cotton wool. It is useful in revealing grain growth in the examination of welded joints.

COPPER AND ITS ALLOYS

(1) *Acid Ferric Chloride Solution*

25 grams ferric chloride, 25 ml. hydrochloric acid, 100 ml. water.

Used for revealing the dendritic structure of the a solid solution.

(2) *Ammoniacal Ammonium Persulphate Solution*
Ammonium hydroxide (0·880) 1 part, ammonium persulphate (2·5% solution) 2 parts, water 1 part.

Used for alloys containing the β constituent.

ALUMINIUM AND ITS ALLOYS

20% Hydrofluoric Acid Solution
The specimen should be degreased with carbon tetrafluoride and then immersed in hot water, prior to swabbing the surface with the etching reagent.

N.B. Particular care should be taken in handling hydrofluoric acid. The acid or its fumes should not be allowed to make contact with the skin or eyes. Etching reagents which contain concentrated acids should only be made up by a responsible laboratory steward or teacher.

SULPHUR PRINTING

The distribution of sulphide inclusions in steels is usually determined by means of a sulphur print. The underlying principle of the test is that dilute sulphuric acid attacks the manganese sulphide inclusions (and ferrous sulphide, if present), liberating hydrogen sulphide gas. This gas reacts with the silver bromide photographic paper, forming a brown stain of silver sulphide. The reactions involved may be represented by the following equations:

$$MnS + H_2SO_4 = MnSO_4 + H_2S$$
$$AgBr + H_2S = Ag_2S + 2HBr$$

It is not possible to obtain sulphur prints from high alloy steels or non-ferrous metals.

The test is carried out by grinding the surface to be examined to about No. 0 grade of emery. It is then thoroughly cleaned and degreased. A piece of bromide photographic paper is soaked in a 3% solution of sulphuric acid in water for about three minutes. This time should not be exceeded since the gelatine tends to swell and the paper becomes very slippery and difficult to keep in position when applied to the steel. The paper is removed from the acid and then lightly pressed between two sheets of blotting paper to remove excess acid. The emulsion side of the paper is then placed in contact with the surface to be examined. With large specimens the paper is placed face downwards on the specimen and usually rolled with a squeegee to obtain close contact and remove air bubbles. With small specimens it is more convenient to place the paper on a flat

141

surface and to press the specimen firmly against it. The time of contact varies with the steel but is usually about two minutes. The intensity of the brown stain can be judged by lifting the corner of the paper. The print is then rinsed in water and 'fixed' in a solution of hypo for ten minutes. It is then washed in running water for twenty minutes and dried.

It is sometimes possible to obtain a second or even a third print from the same surface without further preparation other than washing and drying. The time of contact required, however, is considerably longer.

THE MICROSCOPIC EXAMINATION OF METALS AND ALLOYS

We have seen that useful information can be obtained about the structure of the metal by macro-examination. However, in order to obtain more detailed information, such examination should be supplemented by microscopical examination. Since microscopical examination of metals depends upon the reflection of light from a polished surface, the preparation of the specimen is very important.

PREPARATION OF SPECIMENS

A representative sample should first be obtained from the material being examined. This should be a convenient size for polishing, about $\frac{1}{2}$–1 in. square or diameter where possible. The difficulties encountered in polishing very small specimens may be overcome by mounting them in plastic or a fusible alloy, e.g. Wood's alloy.

GRINDING

The surface to be examined usually contains saw marks and is not perfectly flat. These saw marks can be removed and the surface levelled using a fairly coarse file, or where available a motor-driven linisher. Care should be taken not to overheat the specimen. When the saw marks have been removed the specimen is washed, dried and subjected to fine grinding on a series of emery papers of increasing fineness, i.e. 2, 1, 0, 00, 000 grades of emery. This may be carried out by placing the emery paper on a flat glass plate and holding the specimen so that the scratches are formed in one direction only. Grinding is continued until the scratches left from the previous grinding operation are removed. The specimen is then swilled with water and dried before being transferred to a finer paper. The grinding on the next emery paper is carried out so that the scratches are at right angles to those of the previous paper. Finally a series of fine scratches is obtained in the 000 grade of emery paper, and after washing and drying the specimen is ready for polishing.

For soft metals, e.g. aluminium and magnesium, it is necessary to treat the emery paper with some form of lubricant to prevent particles of emery being embedded in the surface. Typical lubricants are paraffin or a solution of white wax in benzene. It is also advisable to use emery papers that are well worn and smooth for the softer metals and to apply a very light pressure. Suitable wet pregrinders are available on the market which contain strips of emery paper of varying grades clamped to a glass plate. These papers are continually fed with running water which washes away coarse particles. Where large numbers of specimens have to be prepared emery paper fitted to a circular rotating disc may be used.

POLISHING

The fine scratches from the 000 grade of emery paper can be removed by using polishing powders on selvyt cloths. The selvyt cloth may be stretched out on a piece of plate glass or attached to the rotary disc of a polishing machine. Various polishing powders are employed, e.g. jeweller's rouge, alumina, magnesia, and chromic oxide. The use of diamond dust in the form of proprietary diamond pastes with special lubricants produces particularly good results. Metal polishes such as Silvo and Brasso may also be used for copper, brass and soft alloys. After polishing, the specimen should be swilled with water, followed by methylated or industrial spirits and finally dried. Drying can be conveniently carried out using a domestic hot-air hair dryer.

EXAMINATION OF THE POLISHED SURFACE

The polished specimen, with its 'mirror' finish, free from scratches, should then be examined under the microscope in order to observe any of the following:

(1) Cracks
(2) Blow holes
(3) Hard constituents which stand out in relief, e.g. cementite in white cast iron
(4) Non-metallic inclusions, e.g. slag in wrought iron, graphite in cast iron, or manganese sulphide in steels.

At this stage the microstructure of the metal or alloy is not apparent. Light rays from the microscope strike the surface normally and so retrace their path back eventually to the eye.

143

ETCHING

In order to examine the microstructure of the metal or alloy the specimen must be etched. Etching involves the selective corrosion of the polished surface, which renders the various constituents visible by a contrast effect. The specimen is immersed in a suitable etching solution for a given time, removed using nickel or stainless steel tongs, swilled with water and meths, and finally dried. It is then ready for microscopical examination.

Certain corrosion-resisting alloys are frequently etched by means of electrolytic attack. This involves passing a current through an electrolyte containing the specimen as anode and an inert cathode of platinum or graphite.

ETCHING REAGENTS FOR MICROSCOPICAL EXAMINATION
PLAIN CARBON STEELS AND CAST IRONS

1. Nital
2–5% nitric acid in ethyl or methyl alcohol. The etching time varies from a few seconds up to one minute. This reagent is effective in revealing the ferrite grain boundaries but tends to over-etch the pearlite in so doing.

2. Picral
4% picric acid in ethyl alcohol. This reagent does not reveal the grain boundaries but is more effective in revealing pearlite and spheroidized structures.

ALLOY STEELS

1. Mixed Acids in Glycerol
NITRIC ACID 10 ml.
HYDROCHLORIC ACID 20 ml.
GLYCEROL 20 ml.
HYDROGEN PEROXIDE 10 ml.
Suitable for nickel-chromium alloys, austenitic stainless steels and high-speed tool steels. Specimen should be warmed in hot water before immersion.

2. 10% Oxalic Acid Solution (Electrolytic Etch)
The specimen is made the anode with a cathode of stainless steel, graphite or platinum. Use 6 volts for 10–40 seconds. Used to reveal the grain boundaries of 18/8 stainless steels.

COPPER AND ITS ALLOYS

1. 10% Ammonium Persulphate Solution
Must be freshly prepared. Useful for brasses, bronzes and nickel silvers.

2. Acid Ferric Chloride Solution
  FERRIC CHLORIDE 10 gm.
  HYDROCHLORIC ACID 30 ml.
  WATER 200 ml.
Suitable for $\alpha\beta$ brasses, bronzes, aluminium-bronzes and cupro-nickel alloys. Darkens the β phase and thus gives more contrast.

ALUMINIUM AND ITS ALLOYS

1. 1% Sodium Hydroxide Solution
The solution is swabbed over the specimen for 10 seconds.

2. 0·5% Hydrofluoric Acid Solution
This reagent is applied by swabbing with absorbent cotton wool.

3. Keller's Etch
  HYDROFLUORIC ACID 1 ml.
  HYDROCHLORIC ACID 1·5 ml.
  NITRIC ACID 2·5 ml.
  WATER 95 ml.
  This reagent is used for duralumin type alloys. The specimen is usually immersed in the reagent for 10–20 seconds and finally washed in warm water.

NICKEL AND MONEL

The following solution should be freshly prepared before use.
  NITRIC ACID 50 ml.
  GLACIAL ACETIC ACID 50 ml.

TIN AND ITS ALLOYS

1. NITRIC ACID 1 part
  ACETIC ACID 1 part
  GLYCEROL 8 parts
  Use at 40°C. Suitable for tin-lead alloys.

2. NITRIC ACID 1 part
   ACETIC ACID 3 parts
   GLYCEROL 5 parts
   Use at 40°C. Suitable for pure tin.

3. *Acid Ferric Chloride Solution*
   FERRIC CHLORIDE 10 gm.
   HYDROCHLORIC ACID 2 ml.
   WATER 95 ml.
   Used for tin-base bearing metals. Immersion time up to 5 minutes at room temperature.

LEAD AND ITS ALLOYS

1. GLACIAL ACETIC ACID 3 parts
   NITRIC ACID 4 parts
   WATER 16 parts
   Use at 40°C. Etching time depends upon the depth of distorted metal on the prepared surface and varies from 4–30 minutes.

2. GLACIAL ACETIC ACID 3 parts
   30% HYDROGEN PEROXIDE SOLUTION 1 part
   Used for lead-antimony alloys. Etching time 5–20 seconds.

NON-DESTRUCTIVE TESTING OF METALS

The development of methods of non-destructive testing has increased considerably over the past twenty years. Such methods enable an assessment to be made of the quality of the finished component without the use of a test-piece or damaging the component in any way.

Non-destructive tests may be roughly classified as follows:

1. DETECTION OF CRACKS AT OR NEAR THE SURFACE

(*a*) PENETRATION METHODS
(*b*) MAGNETIC CRACK DETECTION
(*c*) ELECTRICAL METHODS

2. DETECTION OF SUBMERGED DEFECTS

(*a*) RADIOGRAPHY   (i) X-RAY EXAMINATION
                     (ii) γ-RAY EXAMINATION
(*b*) ACOUSTICAL METHODS (i) SONIC
                          (ii) ULTRASONIC

1(a) PENETRATION METHODS

Penetration methods involve the introduction of a liquid into the surface cracks by immersion in a suitable penetrant. The penetrant enters the crack and the surface is thoroughly cleaned and dried. The position of the crack is betrayed by subsequent seepage of the penetrant.

Various techniques are employed to obtain good contrast between the stain produced and the background. In the chalk test, the component is soaked in a penetrant such as paraffin, and, after cleaning and drying, the surface is dusted with fine dry chalk. Subsequent seepage of the paraffin from the cracks stains the chalk. Improved contrast can be obtained by the addition of suitable dyes, usually red, to the penetrant. Fluorescent penetrants are also available which indicate the presence of cracks by fluorescence when examined under ultra-violet light.

Surface cracks are also revealed after the anodizing of aluminium alloys (page 137) using chromic acid as the electrolyte. Seepage of the chromic acid from the cracks gives rise to yellow-brown stains on the surface.

Penetrant methods are not as sensitive as magnetic crack detection, but can of course be applied to both magnetic and non-magnetic materials.

1(b) MAGNETIC CRACK DETECTION

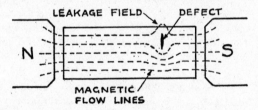

Fig. 15.2. Magnetic Crack Detection

Magnetic crack detection is based on the principle that the defect or crack has a lower magnetic permeability than the metal itself. The magnetic lines of force are thus distorted by the presence of the defect causing a local increase in the magnetic field, known as a leakage field. This leakage field is sufficiently strong to attract magnetic particles, thus revealing the presence of the defect.

In practice the magnetized component is generally immersed in a liquid containing finely powdered magnetic iron oxide in suspension.

The position of the magnetic field relative to the defect is very important (Fig. 15.3). The best indications are obtained when the magnetic field is at right angles to the crack.

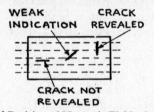

Fig. 15.3. Effect of Position of Magnetic Field relative to the Crack

Magnetic crack detection is widely used for detecting cracks in steels, but obviously cannot be employed for non-magnetic alloys. Sub-surface defects may be indicated but the sensitivity falls off rapidly with the depth of defect.

1(c) ELECTRICAL METHODS

Electrical methods detect cracks by the observation of their effect on the distribution of an electric current flowing in the metal. Two methods may be distinguished:

(i) Direct current resistance method
(ii) Eddy-current method.

In the former method the potential difference between two electrode probes which make contact with the surface is measured using a sensitive spot galvanometer. The presence of a crack between the electrodes causes an increase in potential difference which is revealed by the galvanometer. This method is limited to clean, smooth surfaces since good contact between the electrodes and the surface is essential.

In the eddy-current method a search coil, carrying alternating current, is moved over the surface of the metal and any change in the impedance of the coil is assumed to indicate the presence of cracks. This method is limited to uniform components in the form of bar, strip or tube, particularly for non-magnetic materials. The interpretation of results is difficult and requires considerable experience.

2(a) RADIOGRAPHY

(i) X-ray Examination

This method consists of passing a beam of X-rays through the metal component and studying the effect produced on a photographic film. Defects, such as gas holes and slag inclusions, offer less resistance to the X-rays than sound metal, and their position is therefore indicated on the film by a shadow effect.

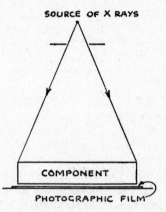

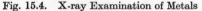

Fig. 15.4. X-ray Examination of Metals

X-ray examination is suitable for the detection of gross defects of dimensions of approximately 1% of the total thickness when the greatest length of the defect lies in the beam direction. Unless the orientation of the defect is known by experience it may be necessary to take the radiographs in a number of directions. X-ray radiography is used extensively for the examination of welded pressure vessels and for gas-turbine blades and aluminium castings. Defects such as gas holes, porosity, slag inclusions, shrinkage cavities and large cracks can be readily detected, but it is not considered a satisfactory method for the detection of very fine cracks. For these, ultrasonic testing is a more reliable method. X-ray examination is expensive and is only used where the cost is justified. Considerable experience is needed for the satisfactory interpretation of a radiograph.

(ii) *γ-ray Examination*

Radiographic examination using γ rays may also be employed, and is capable of detecting the same type of defects as that revealed by X-rays. The method is usually slightly less sensitive, the sensitivity ranging from 1–2%. γ rays are generated continuously by radioactive materials and unlike X-rays, the γ-ray source cannot be 'turned off' after use. Care must be taken to shield personnel from the effects of γ rays.

149

2(b) ACOUSTICAL METHODS

(i) Sonic Methods (e.g. The Hammer Test)

Gross internal defects increase the damping capacity of a metal component. When the metal is hit with a hammer the damping capacity can be roughly assessed by the sound of the note emitted. This method is obviously limited to gross defects and considerable skill and experience are necessary if the results are to be reliable. The method is not suitable for rigid structures due to insufficient resonance.

(ii) Ultrasonic Testing

This method is based upon the principle that the transmission of a beam of ultrasonic waves is upset by the presence of defects in their path. One technique is the 'echo-reflection' method which in modern flaw detectors uses a single probe combining the duties of transmitter and receiver, with the cathode ray oscillograph technique to record the indications. Fig. 15.5(a) shows the indications obtained when the metal is free from defects. When a defect is present some energy pulses return to the probe before those from the boundary and give rise to the indication shown in Fig. 15.5(b).

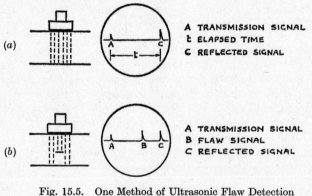

Fig. 15.5.   One Method of Ultrasonic Flaw Detection
(a) Metal Free from Defects
(b) Presence of Flaw in Metal
From *Ultrasonic Flaw Detector Mark 5* (Kelvin and Hughes)

Ultrasonic testing is employed for the inspection of forgings, extrusions, castings, bar stock, welded pressure vessels and rolls.

The interpretation of the instrument indications is difficult and here again considerable skill and experience are required.

Examination Questions

Questions Nos. 1–52 inclusive are taken from past A1 and A2 papers for the Higher National Certificates in Mechanical and Production Engineering at the North Gloucestershire Technical College, Cheltenham. They are included by kind permission of the Joint Committee for National Certificates and Diplomas in Mechanical Engineering.

Questions Nos. 53–67 inclusive have been included for students for the Final City and Guilds Examination in Machine Shop Engineering. Where stated these have been taken from past papers for this examination, by kind permission of the City and Guilds of London Institute. The remaining questions in this group are taken from papers set at the North Gloucestershire Technical College for Final City and Guilds students.

CHAPTERS 1–3

1. Describe, with the aid of diagrams, the mechanism of crystallization of a pure metal. Make neat sketches of the three main types of metallic space lattice, giving examples of metals which crystallize in each type.
2. Explain the fundamental differences between hot-working and cold-working. What are the effects of hot-working on the structure and properties of a mild-steel ingot? Explain the importance of finishing temperature in hot-working.
3. Give an account of the changes which occur during the annealing of cold-worked metals, indicating the factors which affect them.
4. Sketch and explain the microstructure that you would expect upon examination of a specimen of 70:30 cupro-nickel in the cast condition. How would this structure be affected by (1) annealing (2) cold-working after annealing (3) annealing after cold-work?
5. The determination of cooling curves of various alloys of bismuth and antimony gave the following results:

% Antimony	0	20	40	60	80	100
1st Arrest°C.	271	400	490	550	600	631
2nd Arrest°C.	—	285	320	370	450	—

Using the above data draw and label the bismuth-antimony thermal equilibrium diagram.

Describe with reference to a cooling curve the cooling of an alloy containing 50% of each metal, estimating:

(1) the composition of the liquid and solid phases at 420°C.

(2) the relative weights of solid and liquid at 420°C.

What is the effect of rapid cooling on the microstructure of the alloy?

6. Bismuth melts at 271°C. and tin at 232°C. They form a eutectic containing 44% tin which melts at 132°C. Bismuth dissolves a maximum of 4% tin, and tin a maximum of 12% bismuth at the eutectic temperature. Draw and label the bismuth-tin thermal equilibrium diagram. Describe with reference to cooling curves the cooling of alloys containing:

(a) 60% tin

(b) 90% tin from the liquid state to room temperatures.

7. The determination of cooling curves of various alloys of zinc and cadmium gave the following results:

% Cadmium	0	20	40	60	83	90	100
1st Arrest°C.	419	382	345	310	266	280	321
2nd Arrest°C.	—	266	266	266	—	266	—

Using the above data, draw and label the thermal equilibrium diagram for this series of alloys.

With reference to a cooling curve, describe the cooling of an alloy containing 30% cadmium, estimating:

(1) The composition of the constituents present at 320°C.

(2) The relative weight of solid to liquid at 320°C.

(3) The proportion of eutectic in the final structure.

8. Distinguish clearly between the following terms, using diagrams where necessary:

(a) face-centred cubic and body-centred cubic lattice;

(b) eutectic, eutectoid;

(c) substitutional and interstitial solid solution;

(d) liquidus and solidus.

CHAPTERS 4–6

9. Show by means of a graph the effect of carbon content on the mechanical properties of slowly cooled plain carbon steels.

    Compare the microstructures, properties and uses of plain carbon steels containing 0·2%, 0·6% and 1·2% carbon.

10. Give an account of the sulphide inclusions in plain carbon steels.

    Describe how you would determine the distribution of sulphide inclusions along a section of a rolled-steel bar, giving the relevant theory.

11. Discuss the importance of the following factors in the heat-treatment of steel:

    (a) furnace atmosphere;

    (b) control of temperature;

    (c) quenching media and technique;

    (d) design of component.

12. Four specimens of 0·6% carbon steel in the form of half-inch round bar are heat-treated as follows:

    (1) Furnace cooled from 800°C.

    (2) Air cooled from 800°C.

    (3) Water quenched from 800°C.

    (4) Water quenched from 800°C., followed by tempering at 600°C.

    Describe the effects produced on the (1) microstructure
    (2) properties of the steel.

13. Explain briefly, with the aid of diagrams, each of the following terms relating to the heat-treatment of steel:

    (a) Overheating

    (b) Martempering

    (c) Normalizing

    (d) Underannealing

    (e) Sorbite.

14. Sketch and label a typical time-temperature transformation curve (S curve) for a plain carbon steel.

    With reference to this diagram describe the processes of:

    (a) martempering and

    (b) austempering, indicating the advantages and limitations of these processes.

15. Describe with the aid of diagrams the structural changes that occur during:

    (1) the process-annealing of cold-worked 0·15% carbon steel sheet;

    (2) the full-annealing of a 0·5% carbon steel.

16. Write a short account of the process of surface hardening by pack carburizing.

Outline, with reasons, the heat-treatment necessary to develop the optimum properties in a case-hardened component, indicating clearly the structural changes which occur.

17. Give an account of the process of surface-hardening by nitriding. What are the advantages of this method over pack carburizing?

18. Explain clearly the following terms, illustrating your answer with diagrams where necessary:

    (a) burnt steel
    (b) reducing atmosphere
    (c) secondary hardening
    (d) critical cooling rate
    (e) muffle furnace.

19. Sketch that part of the iron-carbon diagram which is of use in the heat-treatment of steels. With reference to the diagram define the terms: full annealing, normalizing, hardening and tempering.

CHAPTERS 7–9

20. State the limitations in the use of plain carbon steels. What are the general effects of alloying elements in steel?

21. Compare and contrast the effect of nickel and chromium as alloying elements in steel.

22. What are the general advantages of alloy steels over plain carbon steels? Give an account of the effect of manganese as an alloying element in steel.

23. Give an account of the composition, properties and uses of the low-alloy nickel-chrome steels. What do you understand by the term 'temper-brittleness'? Indicate briefly how this defect may be overcome or minimized.

24. State typical compositions of alloy steels suitable for each of the following:

    (a) nitriding
    (b) case-hardening
    (c) railway points
    (d) cutlery
    (e) high-speed cutting tools.

    In each case give reasons for your choice and state any heat-treatment which may be required.

25. Give an account of the composition, properties and uses of the austenitic stainless steels. What do you understand by the

term 'weld-decay'? Indicate briefly how this defect may be overcome or minimized.

26. The strength and shock resistance of grey-iron castings is generally inferior to that of steel forgings. Explain briefly the reasons for this and describe two methods of improving the properties of grey cast iron.

27. Give an account of the production, microstructure, properties and uses of each of the following:
    (1) Grey phosphoric cast iron
    (2) Inoculated high-duty cast iron
    (3) White-heart malleable cast iron.

28. State a typical composition for high-speed tool steel. Describe briefly how you would harden such a steel. Make a neatly labelled diagram of the furnace used for this purpose.

CHAPTERS 10–12

29. Sketch and label the copper-rich portion of the copper-zinc thermal equilibrium diagram.

    Show by means of a graph the effect of constitution on the mechanical properties of the brasses.

    What composition would you recommend for (a) deep drawing; (b) hot stamping?

30. Make neat sketches of the microstructure of each of the following, indicating clearly the constituents present:
    (a) 70:30 brass. Cold-worked + annealed condition
    (b) 60:40 brass. Extruded condition
    (c) Admiralty gun-metal. Sand cast condition
    (d) 80:20 cupro-nickel. Cast condition.
    Indicate briefly the chief properties of each of the above alloys.

31. Describe, with reference to the appropriate portion of the copper-aluminium equilibrium diagram, the heat-treatment of a 10% aluminium-bronze alloy, indicating clearly the structural changes that occur.

    What do you understand by the term 'self-annealing'? Indicate briefly how this defect may be overcome or minimized.

32. What are the characteristic properties of aluminium? Indicate how these affect the uses of the metal and its alloys. Classify the alloys of aluminium, stating the approximate composition, properties and uses of *one* alloy in each group.

33. Give an account of the phenomenon of 'age-hardening' with reference to aluminium alloys of the Duralumin type. State the compositions of two other non-ferrous alloys which exhibit age-hardening.

34. What are the characteristic properties of aluminium-silicon alloys? What do you understand by the term 'modification treatment'? What is the effect of this treatment on the structure and mechanical properties of a 13% silicon alloy?

35. What are the characteristic properties of magnesium? Classify the alloys of magnesium and indicate their more important uses.

36. State the composition, properties and one important use of each of the following:
    (a) Monel
    (b) K-Monel
    (c) Inconel
    (d) Nimonic 80.
    Describe briefly the heat-treatment given to (b) and (d) to develop their optimum properties.

37. Write a brief account of *two* of the following:
    (a) Zinc-base die castings
    (b) The Nimonic series of alloys
    (c) The phosphor-bronze alloys.

38. What are the requirements of an alloy to be used as a bearing material?
    State the composition and properties of a typical (1) copper-base (2) tin-base (3) lead-base bearing alloy. Sketch the microstructure of any one of the alloys mentioned.

CHAPTERS 13–15

39. Give a brief account of the electro-chemical theory of corrosion. What do you understand by the 'differential aeration effect' in corrosion? Indicate briefly how this explains the phenomenon of pitting.

40. Explain briefly each of the following terms relating to corrosion:
    (a) Sacrificial protection
    (b) Anodizing
    (c) Season cracking
    (d) Pitting
    (e) Sherardizing.

41. Give an account of the various methods used to protect iron and steel from corrosion.

42. Explain clearly why:
    (a) tough-pitch copper cannot be welded satisfactorily;
    (b) stabilized stainless steel should be specified for welding purposes;
    (c) low hydrogen electrodes are used for the welding of low-alloy high-tensile steels;

(d) pre-heating is essential for the successful welding of a cracked cast-iron component.

43. What are the causes of hard-zone cracking in the welding of low-alloy high-tensile steels? Indicate how this defect may be overcome or minimized.

44. Discuss the effect of hydrogen in the welding of:
    (a) aluminium
    (b) copper
    (c) low-alloy high-tensile steels.

Indicate briefly how these effects may be overcome or minimized.

45. Discuss the advantages and limitations of the various methods used in the non-destructive testing of metals and alloys.

MISCELLANEOUS

46. The compositions of five alloys are given as follows:
    (a) C=0·2%, Si=0·16%, Mn=0·6%, S=0·04%, P=0·04%, Fe=balance.
    (b) C=3·4%, Si=2·5%, Mn=0·8%, S=0·12%, P=1·0%, Fe=balance.
    (c) Al=87%, Si=13%.
    (d) Sn=6%, P=0·2%, Cu=balance.
    (e) Sn=62%, Pb=38%.

State the names by which these alloys are commonly known, and their more important physical properties. Give *one* typical use of each alloy.

47. Outline the method of preparing a specimen of mild steel for microscopical examination, giving reasons for the procedure.

Make neat sketches of the microstructures of a 0·3%, 0·83% and 1·2% carbon steel in the slowly cooled condition indicating clearly the constituents present.

48. Make neat sketches of the microstructures of each of the following, indicating clearly the constituents present:
    (a) 86:10·5:3·5 Sn:Sb:Cu bearing alloy
    (b) Monel metal. Cold worked + annealed condition
    (c) Hadfield's manganese steel. Water quenched from 1,000°C.
    (d) Cast phosphor-bronze.

State briefly the chief properties of each of the above alloys.

49. What do you understand by a peritectic reaction?

Sketch the peritectic portion of the iron-carbon diagram and describe with reference to a cooling curve the cooling of an alloy containing 0·4% carbon from the liquid state until it is just solid.

50. Sketch the complete iron-carbon diagram. With reference to the diagram explain the terms: peritectic, eutectic, eutectoid.

51. Write a short account of *two* of the following:
    (*a*) The effect of nickel in case-hardening steels
    (*b*) Spheroidal graphite cast iron
    (*c*) The isothermal transformation of austenite.

52. Distinguish clearly between each of the following:
    (*a*) Soft solders and silver solders
    (*b*) Fusion and pressure welding processes
    (*c*) Grey and white cast irons
    (*d*) Acid and basic steels.

EXAMINATION QUESTIONS FOR STUDENTS FOR THE FINAL CITY AND GUILDS EXAMINATION IN MACHINE SHOP ENGINEERING (see note on page 151).

53. (*a*) Discuss the applications of commercially pure aluminium in general engineering, and state why this material is seldom used in its pure form.

(*b*) State the effects of (i) copper (ii) silicon when used as alloying elements in aluminium, and give an example of the application of a copper-aluminium alloy, and a silicon-aluminium alloy, stating the approximate chemical composition in each case (C. & G. Final, 1959).

54. The elements molybdenum and tungsten are present in the composition of certain alloy steels. State the particular benefits obtained from the use of either of these in (*a*) small amounts not exceeding 1·5 per cent. and (*b*) large amounts. State the particular applications of steels containing the element selected (C. & G. Final, 1958).

55. (*a*) Discuss the general applications of cast iron as an engineering material, giving three typical examples of its use. State, for each example, the type of cast iron used and its mechanical properties.

(*b*) How does the introduction of nickel into cast irons affect their mechanical and physical properties? (C. & G. Final, 1957).

56. (*a*) What is the essential difference between constructional mild steel and case-hardening mild steel, and what is the reason for such difference?

(*b*) What are the advantages of nickel case-hardening steels over plain carbon steels used for the same purpose? Give the approximate chemical composition of a typical case-hardening steel (C. & G. Final, 1955).

57. The critical temperature of eutectoid steel, according to the equilibrium diagram of the iron-iron carbide system, is usually

taken as 723°C., but satisfactory hardening is not possible with such a steel unless it is water quenched from about 750°C. Explain clearly the reason for this apparent discrepancy between theory and practice.

(b) What would be the minimum hardness value of a fully hardened eutectoid steel? (B.H.N., V.P.H., or Rockwell Scales may be used) (C. & G. Final, 1955).

58. 'White metal' and certain copper alloys are materials used extensively as bearing metals. Give a typical percentage composition for a bearing metal of each material and indicate the service conditions for which each is most suitable (C. & G. Final, 1954).

59. (a) State the advantages and disadvantages of commercially pure aluminium as a general engineering material.

(b) How are the properties of aluminium affected by the inclusion of (i) copper (ii) silicon as an alloying element? (C. & G. Final, 1953).

60. In the heat-treatment of cutting tools, etc., it is often desirable that this should be done without causing scaling of the surface. Describe two methods of achieving this, stating the advantages and limitations in each case (C. & G. Final, 1952).

61. Discuss the general advantages of nickel-alloy cast irons and state the particular advantages when used for:

    (a) small castings of irregular sections which require to be machined

    (b) castings which are to have hardened slideways.

State the type of cast iron used, and the approximate nickel content in each case (C. & G. Final, 1952).

62. Nickel, chromium and molybdenum are elements used in the manufacture of alloy steels. Discuss, in detail, the effects of these elements, both singly and in combination, on the physical and mechanical properties of the steel (C. & G. Final, 1951).

63. What is meant by 'temper brittleness' as applied to alloy steels, and which alloy is particularly susceptible to this phenomenon?

What precautions should be taken in the heat-treatment of such steel to avoid this weakness? (C. & G. Final, 1949).

64. (a) Compare the merits of carbon steel, high-speed steel, cemented carbides and stellite as used for cutting tools.

(b) State the approximate composition of each material.

(c) Describe the heat-treatment you would give to cutting tools made from high-speed steel.

65. (a) Give an approximate composition for:

    (1) an aluminium alloy suitable for aircraft construction

    (2) a brass suitable for cold-working

(3) a bronze suitable for bearings.

(b) Give three examples of cold-working processes.

Explain the effect of cold-working on the material.

66. A steel spindle is required with a hard case and a tough core. What steel would you use?

Explain the heat-treatment necessary and the structural changes that take place in the metal.

67. Grey-iron castings have a limited application due to their low tensile strength. Give particulars of three special irons which have been developed with improved properties. Show, by reference to the structure of the metal, how this has been achieved. What are the industrial uses of these irons?

Questions Nos. 9, 19, 23, 26, 27, 28 and 32 are also suitable exercises for Final City and Guilds students.

Bibliography

1. Institution of Metallurgists, *The Joining of Metals* (lectures delivered at Refresher Course 1951).
2. Institution of Metallurgists, *The Behaviour of Metals at Elevated Temperatures* (lectures delivered at Refresher Course 1956).
3. Institution of Metallurgists, *Year Book and List of Members* 1958–9.
4. American Society of Metals, *Metals Handbook*.
5. Journal of the Institute of Metals, *The History of Magnesium* (paper by MAJOR C. J. P. BALL, July 1956).
6. McGraw-Hill, *Engineering Metallurgy*, MONDOLFO and ZMESKAL.
7. McGraw-Hill, *Applied Metallurgy for Engineers*, BURTON.
8. McGraw-Hill, *Principles of Metallography*, WILLIAMS and HOMERBERG.
9. Arnold, *Metallurgy for Engineers*, ROLLASON.
10. Arnold, *Introduction to Metallic Corrosion*, U. R. EVANS.
11. Pitman, *Engineering Metallurgy*, SISCO (editor). Committee on Metallurgy (New York).
12. Pitman, *High Temperature Alloys*, CLARK.
13. Pitman, *Microscopical Techniques in Metallurgy*, THOMPSON.
14. Pitman, *Engineer's Approach to Corrosion*, TRIGG.
15. Macmillan, *Text Book of Metallurgy*, A. R. BAILEY.
16. John Wiley; Chapman and Hall (London), *Elements of Heat-Treatment*, ENOS and FONTAINE.
17. Chapman and Hall, *Steels for the User*, ROLFE.
18. Chapman and Hall, *Welding of Non-Ferrous Metals*, DR. E. G. WEST.
19. Institute of Metals, *Non-Destructive Testing of Metals*, DR. R. F. HANSTOCK.
20. British Welding Research Association, *Memorandum of the Non-Destructive Methods for Examination of Welds*.
21. Morgan Brothers, *Kempe's Engineer's Year Book*.

22. Blackie, *Metallurgy*, GREGORY.
23. Pitman, *The Heat-Treatment of Steel*, GREGORY and SIMONS.
24. Butterworth, *Metals Reference Book*, Editor, SMITHELLS.
25. English Universities Press, *Engineering Metallurgy*, HIGGINS.
26. Publications by: Mond Nickel Co. Ltd.; Henry Wiggin and Co., Ltd.; The Aluminium Development Association; Copper Development Association.
27. The Association of Light Alloy Refiners and Smelters, *Properties and Characteristics of Aluminium Casting Alloys*.
28. Cooke-Troughton and Simms Ltd., *Photomicrography with the Vickers Projection Microscope*.
29. Kelvin and Hughes (Industrial) Ltd., Publication on *Ultrasonic Flaw Detector, Mark 5*.
30. Griffin, *Process and Physical Metallurgy*, J. E. GARSIDE.
31. Murex Welding Processes, *The Welder*, Coronation number, June 1953.
32. *Journal Iron and Steel Institute*, Vol. 163, p. 277, 1949. Paper by Bardgett and Reeve on Fortiweld Steel.
33. British Standards Specifications.
34. Iliffe, *Metal Industry Handbook and Directory*.
35. Arnold, *Applied Chemistry for Engineers*, GYNGELL.
36. Oxford University Press, *Iron and Steel Today*, J. DEARDEN.

Index

163